Bunch

Let's
Propagate!

Let's Propagate!

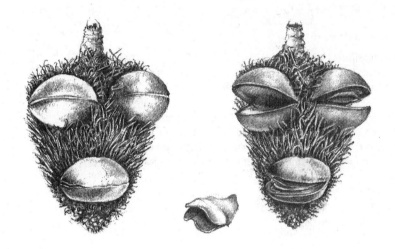

Angus Stewart

ABC
BOOKS

Dedication

To Fred Meyer 1954 – 1999

A great propagator and a great friend

Published by ABC Books for the
AUSTRALIAN BROADCASTING CORPORATION
GPO Box 9994 Sydney NSW 2001

First published October 1999

National Library of Australia

Cataloguing-in-Publication data

Stewart, Angus.
  Let's Propagate: a plant propagation manual for Australia.

  ISBN 0 7333 0350 1

  1. Gardening — Australia. 2. Plant propagation –
  Handbooks, manuals, etc. I. Australian Broadcasting
  Corporation. II. Title

635.91530994

Designed and typeset by Toni Hope-Caten
Illustrations by Deanna Doyle
Cover colour separations by Finsbury, Adelaide
Text colour separations by Moose Colour, Adelaide
Set in 10.5pt/15pt Frutiger
Printed and bound by Australian Print Group,
Maryborough, Victoria

5 4 3 2 1

Acknowledgments

I would like to thank Carolyn Stewart for her inspiration. Thanks also to Thom and Fred Meyer with whom I have shared many years of searching for and propagating all manner of rare and unusual plants. I would also like to acknowledge the work of several people who have been extremely patient and have contributed greatly to the book. They are illustrator Deanna Doyle, photographer Melinda Bargwanna and designer Toni Hope-Caten. Thanks to John Doyle for the inspiration for the book title. Neville Brown (South Africa) and Kingsley Dixon (Western Australia) provided invaluable assistance with the section on smoke induced germination. I would also like to thank various colleagues who have inspired me in plant propagation, Rodger Elliot, Merv Turner, Bob Cherry, Adrian Salter and Ian Gaston. My greatest thanks goes to Stuart Neal of ABC Books who never lost faith in this book.

Thanks to my children—Sarah, Daisy, Emma and Annabel—the propagators of the future.

Let's Propagate!

One of the great pleasures in life is in nurturing living things, and watching them grow to maturity and reach their full potential. One of the easiest ways of deriving this pleasure lies in the propagation and growing of plants in your garden. It is such simple pleasures that have been somewhat lost in our increasingly complex world.

We owe our existence on this planet to plants due to their ability to make their own food utilising the sun's energy. This is all the more remarkable when we consider that when humans are given prolonged exposure to the sun they sometimes develop skin cancer! Thus nature has endowed plants with very different capacities to survive and thrive under harsh conditions. It is, I think, fair to say that plants are one of nature's great filters that can take the wastes of humanity and the rest of the animal kingdom and recycle them into many and varied useful things such as food, timber, flowers, perfumes, medicines and so on. Plant propagation represents one of the ultimate imperatives for us to survive as a species, and it is not surprising that the sight of a new seedling pushing through the soil or strong white roots forming on a cutting invoke child-like excitement in people of all ages.

Plants are remarkable organisms in many ways. Perhaps most amazing of all, though, is their capacity to regenerate from all sorts of bits and pieces. In various plant species, leaves, roots, stems, petals, anthers and, of course seeds, can all give rise to new plants. It is one of the most satisfying and worthwhile pursuits to watch a tiny piece of plant burst into life and proliferate. Many of us look at our neighbours or friends with wonderful gardens and shrug our shoulders and mutter something about them being 'born with green thumbs'. What these people have had usually is the benefit of knowledge and experience from a gardening mentor who has imbued in them an intuitive understanding of how plants grow. I hope that this book may fill this void for those of you who have never had such tuition. I have tried to write it in a fashion that will serve not only new gardeners but also more experienced plant propagators. I have also endeavoured to look at the science behind plant propagation and convert it into a more understandable form for the average reader.

Plant propagation is both a science and an art. By this I mean that there are many factors to do with plant propagation that are able to be measured and quantified very precisely. On the other hand there are many factors that are impossible to predict, let alone control. Perhaps the art of plant propagation is being able to recognise when all the factors in the plant and its environment that influence propagation success reach their optimum (or as close as possible to it).

It is my fervent hope that *Let's Propagate* will provide you with inspiration, encouragement and information to guide you in one of the most rewarding and important activities of all. The plant world provides one of the keys to a sustainable future for humanity, and getting in touch with this world provides each individual with an opportunity to repair our fragile environment.

CHAPTER 1

The Basics of Plant Propagation

Sexual Versus Asexual Propagation

The evolution of plants is a fascinating story that can help us to understand why plants are such malleable organisms when it comes to propagation, as they can reproduce themselves not only by sexual means, but also, in contrast to us animals, by asexual methods such as cuttings. One of the fundamentals that enables life to exist is the ability of plants to harness the sun's energy through photosynthesis. Virtually all other organisms depend on this process for their sustenance. Blue-green algae represent a primitive life form that was most likely the forerunner of the first plant-like organism. Reproduction in these single-celled organisms results from single cells splitting and cloning themselves (i.e. forming exact replicas of the original cell)—asexual or vegetative propagation, in other words. In this instance sex does not form a part of the lifestyle of these organisms. Nevertheless this celibate existence has not stopped blue-green algae from thriving for hundreds of millions if not billions of years. Obviously this reproductive strategy has served blue-green algae well, and the process of asexual reproduction is a natural part of the life cycle of many members of the plant kingdom. **Asexual reproduction** in plants results in the genetic makeup of the parent plant being replicated exactly in the offspring derived from it.

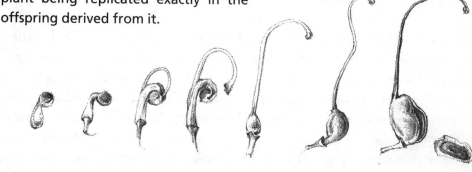

Grevillea 'Robyn Gordon' (left) and its parent *G. banksii* (right).

The offspring of **sexual reproduction** result from the uniting of male and female **gametes** (or sex cells), each one of which contributes half of the genetic material. The genetic material consists of chromosomes that in turn are made up of thousands of individual units known as **genes**. Each gene on the chromosome can exist in more than one form, with the various forms being known as **alleles** of that particular gene. Each of the thousands of genes in a plant has its own individual influence on the form and function of that plant. Being able to combine all the thousands of genes with their alleles in every conceivable combination is what sex is all about. The accidental alteration of genes through mutation is constantly generating even more possibilities for variation. And so it is that sexual reproduction in plants results in an **endless array of new plant forms**.

It is the creation of these new plant forms that has inspired plant breeders and farmers for centuries. The various methods of plant propagation have allowed us to perpetuate forms that would not survive in the wild. For example, the classic Australian garden plant *Grevillea* 'Robyn Gordon' arose as a **chance seedling** on the property of Mr David Gordon in Queensland. A seedling sprang up between two wild species, namely *G. banksii* from Queensland and *G. bipinnatifida* from Western Australia. The story goes that Mr Gordon was going to remove this unwanted chance hybrid, but his daughter Robyn loved the brilliant red blossoms so much that the plant was propagated by cuttings in order to perpetuate it. When Robyn tragically passed away the plant was released to the public under her name. Even though this plant is totally sterile and cannot reproduce from seed, it can now be found in gardens throughout the world thanks to the efforts of plant propagators.

The fact that plants have maintained the ability in most cases to reproduce either sexually or asexually has allowed them to become incredibly successful survivors that are able to colonise and thrive in environmental extremes that would quickly kill most members of the animal kingdom. As plant propagators we can take advantage of the extraordinary plasticity of these remarkable life forms. The choice of whether to use an asexual or sexual method depends very much on the individual circumstance one is faced with. An outstanding individual in a population such as the aforementioned *Grevillea* 'Robyn Gordon' demands to be cloned. In other cases we may be more interested in maintaining genetic diversity and so we choose sexual propagation.

The evolution of flowers in plants can give us further insights into the propagation process. Sexual reproduction presumably arose because of the success of organisms that could produce variable offspring that were able to adapt to changing environmental conditions such as ice ages or indeed global warming. Primitive plants such as mosses and ferns can give us some clues as to how the sexual process began. A typical fern reproduces from tiny structures called **spores** that are borne on the undersurface of the fronds in fruiting bodies known as **sporangia**. The tiny spores are blown about on the breeze and may come to rest in moist, humid conditions where the spores will germinate to produce the sexual stage of the plant's life cycle. This sexual structure looks like a flat, heart-shaped leaf, totally different in appearance to what we recognise as the fern plant. This heart-shaped structure is very fragile and only a few millimetres in diameter. At one end of the heart the female organs or archegonia develop while at the other end the male organs or antheridia are formed. The antheridia release sperm cells that must swim in water to reach the archegonia and fertilise the egg cell contained therein. The resulting fertilised egg grows into the plant that we recognise as a typical fern. This is known as the **sporophyte** stage, and it will develop roots and eventually produce spores. The pro-thallus is known as the **gametophyte** stage, as the sperm and egg cells are produced here through meiosis; collectively they are known as gametes. The one drawback that has tended to limit the spread of these primitive plants is that they must rely on the presence of free water to enable the sperm cells to swim to the egg cells. Thus it is that most ferns and mosses are found growing in cool, moist environments such as rainforests. If we can reproduce these conditions, then we can successfully propagate these plants from spores. The more primitive plant types such as mosses and ferns have been very successful within their limitations—i.e. the need for water to enable the spore cells to fertilise the egg cells. The few types of ferns that have escaped from moist environments are those that have evolved asexual methods of propagation such as the ubiquitous bracken fern which spreads via its vigorous underground stems.

On the other hand the flowering plants that have evolved more recently have developed highly sophisticated structures that enable them to indulge in sexual intercourse in all sorts of weird and wonderful places, from mountain tops to deserts and everywhere in between. Flowering plants differ from more primitive plants in that their seeds are enclosed and protected within an ovary. It is this development that has enabled flowering plants to disperse so widely throughout the world.

Sex Cells!

The Place of Sex in Propagation

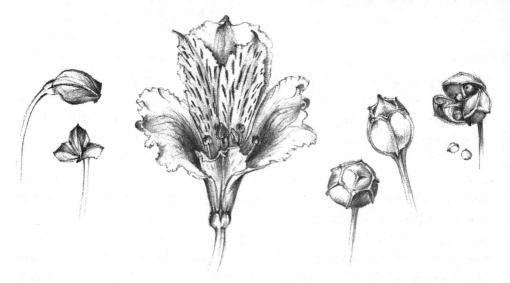

The sex life of plants often makes our own mating games seem rather tame by comparison. Plants have managed to add a whole dimension to their evolution by involving third parties (pollinators such as insects) in their sex lives. These insects are often shamelessly tricked into a sexual relationship with a flower that has not the faintest intention of being faithful to them. Many of these partners often, even unwittingly, give their own sperm or even lives in the name of becoming involved in a torrid, florid relationship.

Flowers are beautifully decorated sexual structures, designed not to appeal to members of the opposite sex but to courtiers that have somehow been convinced to act as go-betweens for them in a way that makes Cyrano de Bergerac look like an amateur. The essential problem for plants is that their sedentary existence makes it impossible for them to have what we would consider a normal sexual relationship. There are, of course, a number of ways by which male and female gametes can be brought together, including wind, rainwater, insects, bats and birds. There are something like a

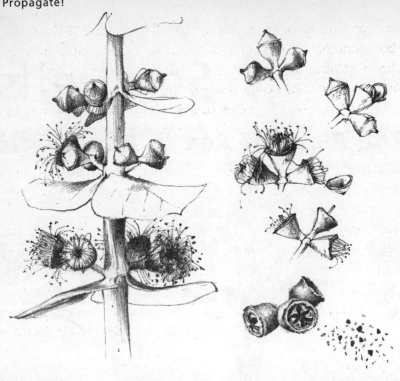

quarter of a million species of flowering plants and this huge number of types has given rise to a bewildering array of possibilities when it comes to transferring the pollen from male to female sexual organs.

The structure of flowers is rather fascinating in itself. The female part is known collectively as the **gynoecium** (from the Greek for 'women's quarters'), and consists of one or more **carpels**, each of which has a hollow ovary at the base that contains the unfertilised **ovules** that may go on to become **seeds**. Each ovary (carpel) has a stalk called the **style** which terminates in the **stigma**, the surface that will eventually become moist and receptive to the pollen. Should the appropriate pollen be received by the receptive stigma, it will germinate and produce a tube that grows through the style until it reaches the ovule and delivers the precious male gamete to be united with its female counterpart.

The male part of the flower is known as the **androecium** ('men's quarters') and consists of structures called stamens that each have a stalk called a **filament** and a sac of pollen called the **anther**. Each pollen grain, of course, contains the male gamete which must somehow find its way to the stigma.

The flower may also have other parts that do not have a direct sexual function but nonetheless may play a dramatic role in the plant's sexual activity. The most obvious of these is the **corolla**, the collective name for the **petals**, those flirtatious organs whose function it is to attract the go-between that will transfer the pollen to the stigma. Petals represent to me one of the pinnacles of evolution in their endless variety, elegance and amazing colourations. Surrounding the petals are the usually leaf-like **sepals**, collectively known as the **calyx**. These are thought to have evolved as a structure to surround and protect the developing flower bud.

The classical model of the flower I have just described can be easily visualised by thinking of a simple rose flower, and it is interesting but perhaps not surprising that this is the view of flowers normally taught to students of botany. The rose is, of course, the archetypal European flower, and it is perhaps for this reason that its structure is presented as the classical model of the flower. I think this is somewhat unfortunate as it often makes it very

A stark contrast between the highly classical flower of the waterlily (*Melinda Bargwanna*) and scarlet banksia.

difficult for people to interpret flowers that do not fit neatly into this classical model. Many Australian plants have flowers that are radically different to this norm, and perhaps this was a powerful reason why early European settlers failed to appreciate the ornamental beauty of plants such as eucalypts, banksias and grevilleas. Indeed, flowers can take on all manner of modifications to the basic structure described above.

The calyx and corolla together are known as the **perianth,** and in some flowers (e.g. grevilleas) the sepals and petals are fused together and are referred to as **perianth segments**. In other cases the petals and sepals have evolved the same appearance so that they all look like petals, as in the hippeastrum (see photo page 107). In this case they are given the special name of **tepal** (an anagram of the word petal). Petals and sepals are actually leaves that have been modified to a greater or lesser extent. Sepals are often green and very leaf-like in their appearance, but they may also be very colourful, as in the NSW Christmas bush (*Ceratopetalum gummiferum*) where the sepals turn bright red as they age. Perhaps their function is to attract something that will eat the mature fruit and then distribute the seed.

In other flowers leaf-like structures called **bracts** may provide additional adornment to the flower. The NSW waratah (*Telopea speciosissima*) provides a classic example, with its dense inflorescence containing hundreds of individual flowers, which in turn are surrounded by large, fiery red bracts that undoubtedly help to attract the bird pollinators that are vital to the sexual process. Another example is the genus *Heliconia*, sometimes known as lobster claws because of the intensely coloured boat-shaped bracts that enclose the flowers in the same style as the flower of the bird-of-paradise (*Strelitzia reginae*), a species to which they are related. Like the waratah, the heliconias are bird pollinated, with the humming birds of tropical America being lured by the amazingly coloured flowers.

As can be seen from the above examples, there are almost endless variations possible in the structure of the flower. What is very important for the plant propagator to appreciate is that flowers were added onto vegetative structures during the long course of the evolution of the flowering plants. Many

The fascinating inflorescence of the waratah with dozens of individual flowers surrounded by petal-like bracts.

of the structures associated with the flower are actually modified leaves, and with many plants there is a rather fine line between the plant producing vegetative or reproductive structures. The change from a vegetative to a reproductive stage in a shoot can be triggered by a number of different factors in different species, with a classic example being short daylength triggering flowering in chrysanthemum and many other species (more correctly it is a lengthening of the night period that actually causes the switch). Once flowering is initiated, the shoot tip undergoes an amazing metamorphosis to start producing the reproductive tissues. Once this happens all sorts of physiological changes occur that make vegetative propagation methods such as cuttings from that shoot much less successful. Thus, this process of change is of great interest to propagators, and observing and recognising the process of change is a very important skill. It is also very important to recognise that the process of flower initiation is reversible and that it is possible to abort the flower bud and have the shoot revert to a vegetative state again. The treatment of flower buds with the group of plant growth regulators known as cytokinins can sometimes reverse floral development, and this can be used to obvious advantage by the plant prop-agator. Conversely, another plant hormone, ethylene, will initiate flower development in a number of species such as pineapples and other bromeliads. Once the delicate balance between vegetative and reproductive growth is understood, it becomes much easier to understand, interpret and manage the patterns of plant growth that are observed through the seasons so that we can better propagate plants from them.

Finally, let us explore the culmination of the sexual process, namely fruits and seeds. Plants that produce seeds (as opposed to spores, as in ferns) are known as **spermatophytes** and there are two basic types of these 'seed plants'. The more primitive type is the **gymnosperm** (from the Greek *gymnos* meaning 'naked' and *sperm* meaning 'seed') such as conifers and cycads, in which the ovules and subsequently the seeds are borne on open scales that are collected together to form familiar structures such as pine cones. The other group of flowering plants is the **angiosperms** (from the Greek *angeion*, meaning an 'enclosure' or 'container', a reference to the ovary which forms the fruit that encloses the seeds). The ovary of the flower

Flowers can take many different forms. Clockwise from top left *Actinotus helianthi* (Melinda Bargwanna), *Protea nerifolia*, *Eucalyptus woodwardii*, *Banksia coccinea*.

can be found at the base of the style and it contains one or many ovules that develop into a seed or seeds. In some rare cases, unfertilised ovules can develop into embryos and give rise to what appear to be normal seedlings but are, in fact, exact replicas of the mother plant. This rare process is known as **apomixis** and occurs in plants such as mangoes and citrus.

The development of the angiosperms represents an enormous evolutionary advance for plants, as the elegantly designed ovary surrounded by all of its beautiful accessories such as petals and colourful bracts attracted all manner of highly mobile pollinators. Thus began a pathway of evolution that continues to generate seemingly unlimited genetic variability and new forms. The diversity of plant forms thus created has enabled the flowering plants to colonise the Earth's land mass from top to bottom. Our challenge as plant propagators is to ensure the survival of as much of this diversity as possible. In order to preserve diversity we must first learn the most important of all the methods of plant propagation—seed.

CHAPTER 3

Propagation by Seed

P ropagation by seed is far and away the most important of all the methods of plant propagation. Of the billions of plants propagated around the world each year the vast majority are done by seed. The list of plants routinely produced by seed is enormous. Cereal crops, vegetables, many fruits, ornamental annuals, lawns and forest trees are all propagated predominantly by seed. Seeds represent one of nature's most elegant evolutionary achievements as they are usually designed to survive the sorts of environmental extremes which would rapidly destroy us animals. There are stories of seeds stored in the pyramids of Egyptian pharaohs that were still viable after many hundreds of years. Even in the hottest deserts seeds will lie in waiting for years and seize upon a brief respite in conditions to complete their life cycle once again. In addition, seeds are produced through a sexual process with a contribution from male and female gametes. This leads to the possibility of genetic variability, something that has led to flowering plants spreading to all corners of the world's land mass. Seed propagation represents perhaps the easiest of all methods and is a great place for the beginner to commence their journey into plant propagation.

Getting started with seed

- **Medium:** The medium should be fairly fine in order to give it a reasonable degree of moisture retention, as the newly germinated seedlings are very susceptible to drying out. 50 per cent fine sand:50 per cent general purpose potting mix will give good results with most species.
- **Container:** All sorts of containers are suitable, but the main consideration is that they should not be too deep (say no greater than 10 centimetres), especially if you are growing smaller seeds. A deep container is generally wasted as seedlings need to be transplanted before the roots can use the medium in a deep pot. An exception can be made for species that have very large seeds (greater than 2 centimetres in diameter) as these can be planted

A foolproof way of watering fine seeded species involves standing the containers in a tray of water. This allows water to move up and avoids the need for overhead watering.

in individual containers because they will form much larger seedlings with expansive root systems in very quick time. The type of container will dictate how many seeds are sown. If the species you are growing has fine roots (e.g. delphinium) that are easily damaged during transplanting, then it may be best to sow one or a few seeds only into a small pot. Then after they germinate thin them out to one per container as soon as they are big enough to handle. For most species, however, an efficient system is to sow lots of seed into a community tray or pot and transplant them into individual containers as soon as they are big enough to handle.

- **Method:** Fill the container loosely to the top and then press down evenly with a suitable flat tamper so that the top of the medium is 1–3 centimetres below the top of the pot (remember that you will be covering the seed with 2–3 times its own diameter of medium). Large seeds are easily handled and can be placed individually on top of the medium before being covered over. For smaller seed, pour the seed into your hand and then take a pinch of seed between thumb and index finger and sprinkle it over the surface of the medium. For extremely fine seed such as many of the begonias, the seed can be mixed with fine sand and shaken onto the medium from a salt shaker in order to achieve more even distribution. The seed should then be covered with 2–3 times its diameter of medium. Some propagators cover seeds with vermiculite as it is sterile (and thus disease free) and retains good levels of moisture around the seeds.

- **Propagation environment:** Seedlings are generally very forgiving when it comes to the environment they are raised in. Evolution has dictated, of course, that only the fittest survive. Species that grow naturally in full sunlight will be quite happy to be germinated in those conditions (but will usually do even better in greenhouse environments), while those from more sheltered environments should be treated accordingly by being grown in either a shade or greenhouse situation. For commercial propagation, greeenhouse production is favoured in order to minimise any problems with extremes of weather such as hail, frost or strong winds. It should also be said that any seedlings grown in the greenhouse will be vulnerable if moved suddenly to more extreme environments outdoors. Very fine seed can be prone to drying out and a useful tip is to cover the container with a sheet of glass or plastic film and keep it out of direct sun. This method can also be complemented by sitting the containers in a tray of water so that they are watered from below by capillary action (this is sometimes known as the 'bog method'). See photo page 22.

- **Time of year:** This will depend very much on the species being grown. Some species can be done at any time of the year, particularly if a greenhouse environment is available. For most species there will be a definite period when it is optimal to sow seed. It is very much a matter of researching the species in question. As a general rule, we try to sow seed at the beginning of the plant's normal growing season. This is absolutely critical if the plant is an annual and, in other words, must complete its life cycle in a matter of months.
- **Things to look for in the propagation stock:** Seed should be free of any pests or diseases. For a number of species some idea of whether the seed is viable can be obtained by putting it in a glass of water. Seed which floats often has not developed properly and is not viable. (This rule does not apply to all species, it should be added.) It is critical to ensure that the seed you are using is predictable from a genetic point of view. Because seed is the result of a sexual process, there is a genetic contribution from a male and a female parent. This means that there is often a possibility of genetic variability within a given seedlot. Plant breeders and seed merchants are well aware of this fact and take steps to control it. It is vital, then, to know the origin of a seedlot in terms of its possible parentage as some unexpected results can occur if open-pollinated (uncontrolled parentage) seed is used. This is discussed further in the theory section of this chapter. Using seed from reputable seed merchants or collecting your own are ways of ensuring predictable results.

Theory

It is a great paradox of the achievement of civilisation and agriculture that we are usually seeking to eliminate the genetic variability that accompanies sexual (seed) reproduction and brings such great advances in yield, disease resistance and other characteristics. Uniformity has become one of the paramount concerns in agricultural and horticultural production, so that products are ready on predetermined dates and fit into standard packaging and so on. Products such as poinsettias for Christmas and chrysanthemums for Mother's Day are all grown from cuttings so that they will be ready within a day or two of market demand.

On the other hand, the extraordinary diversity of the plant world has been the source of a never-ending array of new plant varieties, and plant

Clockwise from top left. Clear labelling is an important requirement in propagation; small quantities of seed are best sown in punnets; commercial production of seedlings.

breeders continually turn back to wild sources for new characteristics. The bind is that as the world's population increases, we must turn more and more towards the uniform varieties which suit mass agricultural production, leaving less and less room for the widespread cultivation and preservation of more genetically diverse plant material. On the other side of the coin, the continued development of these superior varieties will rely on our ability to preserve the gene pools that still exist in the wild. We have perhaps been lulled into a sense of false security about our ability to genetically engineer plants through gene transfers and the like and the idea that this will lessen our reliance on wild sources of genetic variation. The fact remains that the success of modern agriculture and horticulture has been based on conventional plant breeding and domestication of wild plants, a process that continues to this day.

The dangers of a narrowing of the genetic base of a plant were dramatically illustrated by the Irish potato famine. The potato originated in the northern part of South America and the early explorers took but a small sample of the best varieties they could find back to Europe. Consequently all the potatoes in Ireland were genetically very similar and when the conditions were right for the outbreak of soft rot in the crop, all plants were equally susceptible and the population starved as the crop failed. This triggered a wave of emigration that changed the history of places like Australia and the United States.

The preservation of genetic resources is certainly not beyond the average gardener. Throughout history thousands of plant species have been used as a food source. Only a small percentage of those have ever been cultivated intensively and even fewer are grown as major crops today. One has only to think of the Australian Aborigines and the incredible plant diversity that they relied on for food. Of the hundreds, if not thousands of plants they used, only one, the macadamia nut, has become a serious commercial food crop. Farming has increasingly become 'agribusiness', leading to a never-ending quest for profit that compels the farmer to try to maximise profitability from every square centimetre. This in turn leads to the demand for high yielding, uniform plant material, and plant breeders are compelled to meet this objective with their new varieties.

All over the world there has been a disturbing trend for governments to stop funding public plant breeding and seed bank projects, with the argument being that the private sector should be the place for this work. The major problem with this is that private companies are naturally enough mainly motivated by profit and the most profitable strategy is certainly not to maintain hundreds of different varieties of each crop. One would hope that governments around the world could see the long-term benefit in seed banks and arboreta to maintain as much of our precious living plant heritage as possible. Economic rationalism, unfortunately, cannot measure the value of plants that may, one day, be used as a source of disease resistance or adaptability to changing climatic conditions.

Seed Savers While this situation is rather grim, it is not without hope. In addition to public resources such as botanic gardens and seed banks, there are many private individuals and organisations who are actively involved in maintaining the world's genetic resources. The Seed Savers Network, based in Byron Bay, New South Wales, is an excellent example of what can be achieved. This organisation is dedicated to preserving 'heritage' food varieties that are generally unavailable commercially, such as the zebra climbing bean, the Count Zeppelin bean or the Indian cobra melon. A small annual fee is charged for newsletters and unlimited access to the organisation's seed bank, with the idea being that members find their own level of involvement and eventually end up sending seed back to be distributed to other gardeners.

For ornamental plants, there is not quite the same sort of urgency to preserve the genetic material. Nonetheless, the same sort of process of erosion of genetic resources is also occurring in this area. Once again gardeners can play a crucial role in preserving old varieties through organisations such as the Ornamental Plant Collections Association, based in Victoria. The idea of this organisation is to enlist individuals or gardening institutions that will maintain a wide collection of a particular genus of plants such as hydrangeas or eucalypts or whatever. The genes preserved in these ornamental plants may even prove to be valuable as a source of new variability that could be introduced to crop plants through genetic engineering in the future. At the very least the preservation of old varieties of ornamental plants will provide plenty of pleasure to the gardeners of the future.

Seed Collection

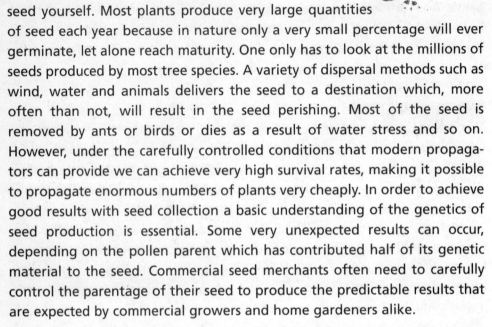

Perhaps one of the most satisfying of all plant propagation pursuits is collecting and subsequently growing seed yourself. Most plants produce very large quantities of seed each year because in nature only a very small percentage will ever germinate, let alone reach maturity. One only has to look at the millions of seeds produced by most tree species. A variety of dispersal methods such as wind, water and animals delivers the seed to a destination which, more often than not, will result in the seed perishing. Most of the seed is removed by ants or birds or dies as a result of water stress and so on. However, under the carefully controlled conditions that modern propagators can provide we can achieve very high survival rates, making it possible to propagate enormous numbers of plants very cheaply. In order to achieve good results with seed collection a basic understanding of the genetics of seed production is essential. Some very unexpected results can occur, depending on the pollen parent which has contributed half of its genetic material to the seed. Commercial seed merchants often need to carefully control the parentage of their seed to produce the predictable results that are expected by commercial growers and home gardeners alike.

In the wild a degree of genetic variability within a species is vital to enable adaptation to long-term changes in the natural environment. Many species of flowering plants have evolved colourful and unusual flowers to attract insects and animals which ensure cross pollination between individuals within a species. A good way to visualise this process is to look at the human parallel. The human species has evolved powerful social taboos to ensure that individuals do not breed with their immediate family. This is presumably because such inbreeding can sometimes result in individuals who inherit disease-causing recessive genetic characteristics. Normally these recessive characteristics (or alleles) are masked by dominant characters, as it is improbable that two unrelated individuals will carry the same recessive allele for one of these nasty characteristics. For most plants, breeding with unrelated individuals of the same species gives a much greater chance of producing strong, healthy offspring. Just look at the brothers and sisters in a typical family—they are similar in appearance to each other and their parents, but yet are still clearly different (unless, of course, they are identical twins).

When seeds are produced from uncontrolled pollinations we can expect a similar amount of variation to that exhibited in a human family (except in the case of self-pollinating plant types, such as grasses which we will cover later in this chapter). In some cases this variability is not a problem, such as in the home garden, where minor variations in flower colour, plant size or shape can be tolerated or even welcomed. In other situations, such as commercial production, this variability can be disastrous, and in such cases being able to control the parentage of the seed becomes much more important.

Open pollination

If parentage of seed is unknown, it is referred to as open pollinated—the male parent is unknown. In such cases the would-be seed collector takes something of a risk as to the genetics of the seed, and it perhaps should be assumed that the seedlings will show a signifcant amount of genetic variability. Whether this variability will be a problem will depend on the end usage; for the home gardener this variation may be a source of great interest and excitement as each individual plant flowers. When collecting such seed it is wise to observe the plants growing nearby which may have been the male parents. If, for instance, you are collecting tree or shrub seed, then it is wise to check that there are no other related species nearby that may hybridise with the species you are collecting. Eucalypts are an interesting example as there are hundreds of species in the genus, many of which will readily hybridise with each other. I have had a significant number of chance hybrid seedlings occur in seed I have collected from street trees growing amongst other eucalyptus species. To guard against this, a grove of trees of the same species growing in isolation will be the ideal source. Seed collected from the wild will usually be true to type, although hybridisation can and does occur in nature where there is a mixture of species growing together.

An interesting example of the consequences of open pollination is the policy adopted by most, if not all, botanic gardens around the world. Botanic gardens are normally concerned with the preservation of species which have been collected in the wild. These species are then brought together and cultivated side by side. The seed set by the plants growing in these collections is regarded as useless for the purposes of perpetuating each species because of the great probability that the species growing side by side will cross pollinate and hybridise with each other. Only if controlled pollinations are carried out can there be any confidence in the genetic identity of the seed.

Self-pollination

I suggested earlier that cross pollination is the general rule with plants as it helps ensure genetic diversity within a species which in turn gives it the capacity to evolve and adapt to changing environmental conditions. There are, however, important exceptions to this situation. A number of important plant groups such as the grasses (which includes cereals such as wheat and rice and many others) have adopted a different approach to evolution. These plants are known as **obligate inbreeders** (i.e. they are virtually obliged to be self-pollinating) and their flowers have developed forms which greatly increase the likelihood of pollen from the same plant fertilising its female structures and then setting seed. In this case the offspring are very uniform genetically and all the deleterious recessive characteristics tend to have been bred out of the population. The result is seedlots that are very uniform and very cheap. This gives particular 'lines' of seed which are uniform within the species, so collection of seed from species which are normally self-pollinating is generally reliable for seed collectors.

Inbreeder	Preferentially an Inbreeder	Preferentially an Outbreeder	Outbreeder
Impatiens	Aster	Ageratum	Aquilegia
Sweet Pea	Dahlia	Cornflower	Begonia
Dwarf Bean	Salpiglossis	Delphinium	Petunia
Lettuce	Snapdragon	Verbena	Polyanthus
Tomato	Salvia	Cabbage	Primula
	Leek	Cauliflower	
	Swede	Cucumber	
		Raddish	

Cross pollination

In this situation it is known that self-pollination has not occurred and male and female parents are genetically different. Some species are **obligate outbreeders** (a fancy way of saying that self-pollination is virtually impossible) and their flowers have evolved mechanisms to ensure cross pollination—for instance, in some species the stigma is genetically programmed to produce chemicals that are lethal to pollen from the same plant. With such species, cross polination is achieved by simply growing the desired parents together in isolation and letting the bees do the rest. Obviously the seedlings produced from this seed will tend to show lots of variation which may or may not be a problem, although in this case there is very little that can be done short of resorting to vegetative propagation (which is only feasible for perennials, as for annuals and biennials it is uneconomic when compared with seed propagation).

We have looked above at **obligate inbreeders and outbreeders** but there are yet other groups of 'breeders' to consider, namely **facultative inbreeders and outbreeders**. Facultative breeders are able to do it either way, self or cross pollination, giving them a somewhat enviable array of choices for sexual satisfaction! Facultative outbreeders have flowers which favour cross pollination, but if no pollen arrives then self pollination occurs. On the other hand, facultative inbreeders will usually self-pollinate but will also quite happily produce seed when cross pollinated. Obviously for this group of plants it is very important to know whether they have been selfed or crossed. If selfed seed is required, then the seed parent plant must be grown in a situation that prevents self-pollination, such as an insect-proof cage.

The Practicalities of Collecting Seed

Seed collection is one of the most satisfying of all tasks for the propagator, as this is where it all starts. Choice of the seed parent plant is all-important from a genetic point of view, and the preceding section of this book on pollination should be read in order to understand how to get the result you require. Genetic off types (where plants display unexpected genetic variability) can be absolutely disastrous, particularly when you are dealing with trees which may live for hundreds of years.

Seed collecting equipment

Various tools of trade will make seed collection and sorting much more efficient and enjoyable. Fruit picking aprons are designed to enable a large quantity of fruit to be picked and carried from plant to plant while leaving both hands available to speed up the process. Once the apron is full, the clips are undone and the contents emptied. Extendible branch loppers, see photo below and fruit picking ladders (for safety's sake work in pairs if ladders are being used in remote locations) will greatly assist in collecting from shrubs and small trees. Various devices are available for climbing trees such as life lines and climbing irons (your local tree surgeon is a good person to consult about what is available in this line).

A tarpaulin or upside down umbrella is particularly useful for catching seed which sheds as soon as it is ripe. Alternatively, a large square of light fabric such as a cotton sheet tied at the corners to bamboo poles can be raised underneath seed-bearing branches of plants where the fruits or seeds can be easily shaken off the branch. 'Cherry pickers' are machines that consist of mobile platforms that can be raised and lowered to desired heights. They are

Left: An extension pruner is used to collect eucalyptus seed capsules. Right: The dehiscent seed pod of this bignonia needs to be enclosed in a stocking to prevent seed being lost.

normally used by electricity workers to service power lines but are equally useful for seed collection purposes, although they are prohibitively expensive to purchase or hire. For very valuable seed on tall trees such as the Wollemi pine, helicopters have been used to dangle the seed collector into the canopy to collect seed—this is obviously a rather dangerous exercise that should only be performed by very experienced operators. An alternative for tall trees is to use a high powered rifle to shoot off seed-bearing branches— a technique perfected by seed collectors working on eucalypts. Another somewhat unconventional piece of seed collection equipment is a vacuum cleaner—this can be particularly useful in situations where seed is in the process of being shed by the plant. It perhaps goes without saying that one should empty the vacuum cleaner bag before attempting this method.

Dry dehiscent

Fruit types

A knowledge of the different fruit types that flowering plants produce is the starting point for efficient seed collection. Botanically speaking, a fruit is the seed-bearing structure developed from the ovary of an angiosperm (flowering plant) after fertilisation. There are numerous variations of fruit structure which give rise to a long list of complicated and difficult to grasp fruit names such as circumsissile capsules, schizocarps, siliquas and samaras. These different types are created on the basis of characteristics such as the attachment of the seeds to the ovary wall and the way that the fruit opens (or does not open) to release the seeds. While botanists will find these different fruit types invaluable in their quest for identifying and classifying plants, propagators, on the other hand, often do not need to appreciate these fine botanical distinctions between fruit types. Reference should also be made here to the gymnosperms (the name means 'naked seeds') which, to a botanist, do not produce a true fruit (where the seeds are enclosed) because these plants do not produce ovaries as such. Most of the gymnosperms, for example pine trees, produce woody cones and have therefore become known as conifers. I would propose then, for plant propagators, that a far more useful way of classifying the various seed-bearing structures is:

1. Dry structures that split apart (dehisce) to release their seed at maturity. Examples here include various types of pods such as the legumes of the

Dry dehiscent

pea family, capsules from plants like poppies and cones from various gymnosperms (or conifers).

2. Dry structures that do not split apart at maturity (indehiscent). Examples here include the achenes of the daisy family and the caryopsis of the grass family.

3. Fleshy structures that do not split apart at maturity (indehiscent). Many fruits and vegetables fall into this category, with the stone fruits like peaches and apricots providing an obvious example. In this case, the seed is surrounded by succulent, fleshy tissue that normally attracts suitable creatures that will eat the fruit and thereafter distribute the seed.

Dry indehiscent

Drawing a distinction between these groupings is useful because it enables the seed collector to decide how to handle a particular plant species when the fruits or seed-bearing structures mature. For group 1, which sheds its seeds as soon as they mature, collection poses some problems, particularly if the plant bearing the seed is in an awkward site. In such cases it may be very difficult to be there at the right time. If seed is harvested before it is shed, you run the risk of it not being ripe. On the other hand, wait too long and you will be crawling around on your hands and knees looking for the proverbial 'needle in a haystack'. The thing to look for is the change in colour of the fruit that accompanies maturation of the seed within. For most species the first hint of darkening of the fruit can be a suitable compromise. A small percentage of the seed may still be too immature to germinate, but generally a satisfactory result can be obtained. Another trick is to enclose the immature fruit in a porous material which will catch the seed as it is shed. An old stocking or muslin bag is ideal for this purpose, as it still allows the passage of air to ensure that the fruit does

Dry dehiscent

Opposite page: The woody seed capsule of the mottlecah *(Eucalyptus macrocarpa)* takes many months to develop after pollination. *Melinda Bargwanna*

not go mouldy. It is not always possible or practical to bag fruits, however, and in such cases a tarpaulin underneath the plant is another option. Beware of animals which might be interested in the seed also, as ants, birds and others will be quick to pounce on the feast that you will conveniently collect and display for them.

Stockings for your plants?

One of the more amusing experiences of my plant propagation career was an episode where I was purchasing some stockings so that I could bag some ripening grevillea fruits. As I took the stockings to the supermarket checkout, the operator looked knowingly at them and said, 'For your wife, of course?'. To which I answered, 'For my grevillea, actually'. The look on her face was worth bottling.

The second group, with dry fruits that do not shed their seed when they ripen, is a much easier proposition (for obvious reasons). Many Australian species, such as eucalypts, bottlebrush and hakeas, have fruits in this category. In these particular plants the woody fruits are an adaptation to protect the seed from fire and other environmental catastrophies. The fruits of these plants will survive the most intense of fires unscathed and then, as soon as the branch they are on has died, the fruit opens up and scatters seed onto the nice, clean, nutrient enriched seed bed below. The magnificent mountain ash (*Eucalyptus regnans*), the tallest flowering plant in the world, has perfected this survival strategy in the cool, moist cathedral-like forests of Victoria and Tasmania. For species with dehiscent fruits, simply collect the fruits and place them in a paper bag in a warm, dry place until they shed their seed. For a number of species, such as banksias and hakeas which live in fire prone environments in the wild, further encouragement can be provided by a gentle tickle from a blowtorch, or an hour or so in a warm oven (say 70 –100 degrees Celsius). Once the seed has been shed, it can usually be easily cleaned by putting the mixture in an appropriately sized sieve.

Opposite page: Grevilleas set copious amounts of seed which can be easily collected by placing a stocking over the developing seed pods. The progeny of grevilleas can be quite different to the parents, often in exciting ways. For exact replicas, grevilleas can be propagated by semi-hardwood cuttings.

Dashboard dehiscence

For a number of species where the fruit opens up after removal from the plant an ideal method involves taking advantage of the high temperatures generated on the dashboard of your car on a sunny day. Simply place fruits of plants such as eucalypts, banksias and hakeas in a paper bag and leave them on your dashboard in direct sun. A few hours of this treatment and the fruits will open and release their seed with a minimum of fuss. A sieve can then be used to separate the seed from the fruit.

For both of the above groups with dry fruits, the actual drying process after collection is a fairly simple matter. If the fruits are subjected to some sort of heat such as that of an oven to get them to open, then the seed will be dried during this process. An alternative is to spread the seed on a towel or tissue paper and leave it in the sun for a few hours. It is absolutely vital that the seed is dry before it is put into airtight storage as it will quickly go mouldy if there is any hint of moisture. The third group with fleshy fruits has evolved with a very different strategy for seed distribution. Most fleshy fruits do not readily release their seed and in nature an animal usually eats them and the seed is distributed in the manure or spat out at a location some distance from the parent plant. In fact, for a number of plant species, germination is considerably enhanced by its passage through the animal's gut. Chemicals such as strong acids are prominent in the stomach of most animals and the interaction of the seed with these chemicals presumably breaks their dormancy.

Cleaning of seeds from fleshy fruits poses entirely different problems when it comes to the extraction process. Perhaps the best method entails mashing the fruit in water and then straining it through a suitably sized sieve while using running water to wash away the remaining pulp. For moderate quantities of seed, a kitchen blender set on low speed is often suitable, provided the seed is not damaged during the process. The seed can

Fleshy
indehiscent fruit

...hough it is ...many fleshy ...as soon as ...ively, stored ...s dampened ...here rinsing ...for going ...urther treatment ...er for days or even weeks will result in ...rmentation process to occur, which in ...pulp, making it much easier to extract

Fleshy Fruits

The world her-...ensland is home to that remarkable ...ghtless bird is somewhat reminiscent ...ly different habitat. Its diet consists ...forest plants such as lilly pillies. The ...gested in the gut, leaving the seed ...he manure. The chemical treatment ...l to breaking dormancy in a number ...ssowary also provides a vital link in ...within the rainforest.

Tips

1. **After washing fleshy fruited seed, spread the seed out on tissue paper to dry. When it has dried the seed will be firmly stuck to the tissue paper. The tissue can then be torn into small pieces with each containing a separate seed. This stops the seed sticking together and makes for much easier sowing.**

2. **When washing seed it will often be noticed that some seeds float while others sink—usually the floaters are hollow because they are lacking in food reserves (endosperm) and should be discarded.**

Seed cleaning

The process of cleaning seed involves separating the seed from any debris from the fruit that is left after the initial collection of the seed from its parent plant. A great variety of equipment and tools is used to clean seed but most, if not all, of this gear can be provided by improvising with commonly available household items. (A word of warning though—the use of kitchen utensils may cause some disturbance to other members of the household and therefore could be hazardous to your health.) Useful equipment is listed below:

- Sieves. A range of mesh sizes is needed from extremely fine to coarse as seeds come in an endless array of sizes and shapes—from coconuts to the seed of orchids, which is like microscopic dust. Great care should be exercised in ensuring that the sieves are thoroughly cleaned between each seed lot, for obvious reasons.
- Drying racks. A cardinal rule is that newly collected seed (with its associated debris) should not be bulked together and stored without first drying it thoroughly to prevent fungi, bacteria and insects from spoiling it. Most seeds should be dried on mesh racks, canvas or trays, or at the very least in hessian sacks that are hung in a well-ventilated area.
- Rubbing boards. Often constructed of timber, these devices are essentially single ended troughs where the fruits are rubbed within the trough by a trowel-like hand tool. Once as much seed as possible has been freed from the fruits, the trough may be emptied into a sieve that will help sort the seed from the chaff.
- Fans. Seed that has been threshed (released) from its fruit may also be separated from the debris by the process of **winnowing**. Seed and chaff is thrown gently in the air and a fan blows away any light debris and hopefully leaves the heavier seeds to fall back down ready for storage.
- Buckets. Fleshy fruits are usually cleaned by washing the pulped flesh away or by fermenting the fruits until such time as the flesh dissolves away from the seeds. Buckets are sufficient for small quantities of seed, while long troughs may be necessary for larger quantities.

Seed storage

The length of time that the seed of a particular species can be stored varies enormously and is often a reflection of the way the seed works in the wild. For instance, most rainforest species have seeds that germinate as soon as they are ripe. The seedlings then grow very, very slowly on the forest floor, waiting for a gap in the canopy to allow them enough light to grow more rapidly and fill that gap. Thus seed of these species does not store particularly well and should be considered as short-lived. In a sense these species maintain a genetic bank as seedlings rather than as seed. At the other extreme, species such as wattles (*Acacia* species) that are found in drier, fire-prone areas have evolved extremely hard and impervious seed coats that enable them to survive droughts and bushfires. Seed of such species can be stored for many decades under the right conditions. In considering the issue of seed storage then, the first consideration is the genetic potential for longevity.

Seed longevity of most plant species, even short-lived ones, can be significantly increased by understanding their ecology and storage requirements. Many short-lived seeds are fleshy in nature with permeable seed coats and have high moisture contents (up to 50 per cent in some species) that must be maintained if the seed is to be successfully stored for any length of time. Therefore, for such species as macadamia nut (*Macadamia integrifolia*), black bean tree (*Castanospermum australe*) and oaks (*Quercus* species),

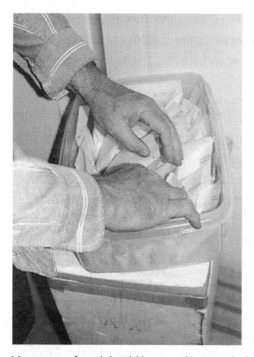 

Most types of seed should be stored in 'snap-lock' plastic containers in a refrigerator or cool room.

seed should be stored in moist sand or peat moss and generally speaking at low temperatures such as 5 degrees Celsius in order to prevent germination. For longer-lived seeds, the moisture content of the seed can drop much lower, and for these species the ideal is to dry the seed out to moisture levels of around 5 per cent and store them at low temperatures (2 to 5 degrees Celsius) and constant low relative humidities of around 20 to 25 per cent. This can be achieved fairly readily by firstly making sure that seed has been properly dried and then storing it in an air-tight container, such as a plastic 'cliplock' bag, in a refrigerator. Humidity levels can be kept constant through the inclusion of a dessicant (moisture absorbing chemical) such as silica gel in the container in which the seed packets are stored. Large plastic food storage containers with snap-on lids are excellent vessels for storing seed packets.

Seed testing

The viability of seed will obviously have a critical effect on the success of seed propagation and storage. There are a number of methods that can be used to help determine seed viability, with varying degrees of complexity. Some of the simpler methods include:

- Placing the seed in water and discarding seeds that float (indicating that they are hollow and lack an endosperm or food source). This method is not applicable to all species as in some cases all the seed will float whether it is viable or not. The method works best for larger, fleshy seeds.
- Dissecting samples of seed and examining the inside of the seed. Firm white flesh inside the seed generally indicates viable seed. For small seeds magnification may be needed to adequately examine the seeds.
- Germination testing. A given number of seeds, usually100, is placed onto a suitable medium such as moist tissue paper or cotton wool in an incubator or other suitable environment. The number of seeds that germinate under these conditions is counted and used to calculate a **germination percentage**. This is a very useful statistic as it enables the propagator to estimate what quantity of seed will need to be sown to generate a given number of seedlings.
- Tetrazolium testing. Seeds that have difficult or unknown dormancy requirements make life difficult for the would-be seed tester. One way of testing whether the embryo of a seed is still alive is by using a chemical stain called tetrazolium, which turns living tissue a red colour

while non-living tissue remains uncoloured. If the whole embryo turns red then viability is fairly certain. If any parts of the embryo are not stained, it may indicate problems such as pathogen attack on the embryo. Details of this test can be found in *Plant Propagation– Principles and Practices* by Hartmann and Kester (See Further Reading).

■ Excised embryo test. In this test the embryo is removed from the seed and placed on a suitable medium to see if there are any signs of growth. This test becomes more difficult the smaller the seed (and therefore the embryo). Glass or plastic petri dishes are lined with moist filter paper or cotton wool, and the embryos are placed on this. Great care must be exercised when removing the embryo as it is easily damaged; sharp scalpels and forceps are the ideal tools for the job. Non-viable embryos tend to brown off or go mouldy very quickly, while viable embryos will remain white and healthy and may start to grow and produce chlorophyll. This test is particularly useful for seeds that have long dormancy periods.

Mountain Ash Shoot Out

Certain species pose great difficulty to the would-be collector. For instance, the mountain ash (*Eucalyptus regnans*) from the moist forests of Tasmania and Victoria is the tallest flowering plant in the world and its gumnuts are borne tens of metres in the air. In cases such as this extreme measures are called for, such as the use of high powered rifles to blast off whole branches.

Wollemi Pine Chopper

Dangling the seed collector out of a helicopter into the seed-bearing canopy is a technique used to rather dramatic effect to collect seed from the Wollemi pine (*Wollemia nobilis*), which was discovered in late 1995. There are only two very small stands of the tree left in the wild and they both occur in deep gorges in isolated sandstone country in a national park to the west of Sydney. Use of a helicopter was initially thought to be the most effective way to collect seed, but it was fairly quickly established that the danger to both collector and trees was too great, given the narrowness of the gorges. Instead, an extensive network of tarpaulins was set up underneath the trees and this has also proven relatively effective.

Can I Collect Seed from F1 Hybrids?

Technically speaking an F1 hybrid is simply the first generation of a hybrid cross of one genetically unique individual with another (they may be from the same or different species). Succeeding generations derived from the F1 hybrids are known as F2, F3, F4 and so on. Somewhere along the line, however, the term F1 hybrid has increasingly been used to refer to a particular method of producing superior hybrid strains of particular annual crops such as certain flowers and vegetables. The basic idea behind F1 hybrids is that two separate breeding lines are developed by self-pollinating each line for many generations, thereby 'fixing' certain genetic characteristics in them (in other words, making them genetically homozygous). The two breeding lines thus produced are then crossed together to produce the F1 seed strain. This hybrid strain is usually incredibly vigorous and genetically superior in its performance. In this case the whole is much greater than the sum of the two parts, due to the phenomenon of **heterosis** or **hybrid vigour**. Generally speaking the crosses between genetically dissimilar individuals produce the greatest hybrid vigour, and this is the idea behind F1 hybrid seed where the two genetically different parent breeding lines are finally crossed together. This perhaps explains why saving seed from F1 hybrids often yields very disappointing results as the genetically similar F1 seedlings pollinate each other. This usually results in a large range of types that cover the spectrum between the two parent seed lines initially used to produce the F1 seed strain. The comment is often made that you cannot save seed from these F1 seed strains. In most cases though, it is possible to save seed but the propagator must realise that they will not come true to type. In many situations the resulting variability may be unacceptable and the end result will be vastly inferior than if fresh F1 seed is used.

Commercial Seedling Production

Large-scale production of seedlings very readily lends itself to mechanisation through the use of vacuum seeding machines that can plant tens of thousands of seeds each day. The production of bedding plants, cut flower and vegetable seedlings and forest trees is normally done in rigid plastic cell trays. The number and depth of the cells in a tray can be varied to suit the particular type of seedling being raised. Tree seedlings, for instance, are raised in much deeper and broader cells than say annual bedding plants.

Vacuum seeders rely on a row of hollow needles to which a vacuum is applied. This enables each needle to suck a seed onto its end. The row of needles is then moved to the cell tray and the vacuum is removed, allowing the seeds to drop onto the surface of the medium in the cells. The tray is on a conveyor belt and this moves it through row by row for the cells to be sown. After the seed is sown it must be covered with a suitable medium such as vermiculite before it is watered. Some vacuum seeders are equipped with attachments that cover the trays and then water them and they emerge at the end of the conveyor belt ready to go straight into the greenhouse. In some seedling nurseries the trays of seedlings are put onto racks in a movable shelf system and the whole thing is moved to a germinating room where the temperature and humidity are very precisely controlled. Once the seedlings have germinated, they are taken straight to a greenhouse where they are laid out on the growing benches. The vacuum seeding process is extremely efficient and seedlings can often be produced for a few cents each, making this by far the cheapest method of propagation.

Vacuum seeding machines are used commercially to automate the process of seedling production.

Seed Dormancy

Plants have managed to colonise all but the most extreme of environments. Even in seemingly impossible situations such as deserts and mountain tops, certain plants have found ways of coping with the stresses. Seeds provide a way in which plants can avoid freezing winters or regular summer droughts. **Dormancy** can be defined as that state when a viable seed that is provided with all the basic requirements for germination such as moisture, oxygen and suitable temperatures still fails to germinate. There are a number of different dormancy mechanisms and the great challenge to plant propagators is to break dormancy. If we pause for a moment to consider why nature has invented seed dormancy the answer is rather obvious. If all the seed from a given season germinated at once and then some sort of environmental stress such as heavy frost occurred, the whole year's seed crop would be wiped out. On the other hand, dormancy allows nature to produce seedlings at a time that is most favourable for their establishment. Presumably, dormancy mechanisms in various species have evolved through natural

Smoke production used to break dormancy in a number of species from South Africa, California and Australia. *Neville Brown*

selection eliminating plants whose seeds germinated immediately after being shed and then struck environmental stress and died. It is interesting to note that species which have been in cultivation and have been subjected to intensive plant breeding do not usually have dormancy problems. This is presumably because plant breeders have reversed the natural selection process and eliminated seeds which didn't germinate immediately.

Hard seed coat dormancy

Most of the Australian wattles (*Acacia* species) have seeds with very hard coats which are impervious to water. The seed is ejected from the pods when it is ripe and is often harvested by ants for the nutritious elaisome which is attached to the seed. The ants eat the attachment and discard the inedible seed which then lies in wait for something to break its dormancy. The fierce heat of a bushfire passing over will crack open the seed coat and release the dormant embryo inside. In addition the ash from the fire provides extra nutrients, and the lack of competition from older shrubs destroyed by the fire creates the perfect seed bed. Nature provides a beautiful example from which to learn! Many other species from harsh environments also display hard seed coat dormancy.

Smoke enhanced germination

A great puzzle for propagators of Australian plants over the years has been the apparent impossibility of germinating a number of species. Plants such as the spectacular black kangaroo paw (*Macropidia fuliginosa*) of Western Australia simply defied anyone to propagate it by seed. A standard recommendation was to plant it in a punnet, stand it outside in full sun and forget about it, looking at it every year or so in the forlorn hope that nature may have grinned at you. Similar puzzles were exercising the minds of propagators of native vegetation in other parts of the world with similar climates and vegetation types to Australia's, namely the South African Fynbos and the Californian Chapparal country. Not only were there similarities in climate and vegetation type, but also the occurrence of regular wildfires was a shared characteristic. Propagators had long known about the effects of heat on physically cracking open the hard seed coats of plants such as wattles (*Acacia* species). The factor which had escaped propagators was the smoke and its after-effects. It has now been established conclusively that many species from these three areas will only germinate reliably after chemicals released by smoke have penetrated the seed coat. Like most great discoveries the idea seems so simple and obvious that one wonders why it took so long to figure out! (See Appendix 1 on smoke enhanced germination for more detailed information.)

Chemical inhibitor created dormancies

Another fascinating dormancy puzzle that has its answer in a complex ecological web lies in the rainforests of northern Queensland and New Guinea where the giant bird, the cassowary, roams the forest floor. A feature of the shrubs and trees of rainforests around the world is their succulent, fleshy fruits which are irresistible to birds and other animals. This is a tremendous example of co-evolution, as the animals benefit from distributing the seed as widely as possible to ensure their future food supply, while the plant species ensures its ongoing survival. Increasingly, scientists are discovering that human impact on rainforests is reducing the range of the cassowary, thus creating a downward spiral in the rainforest as the seeds of survival are no longer being distributed as before. A ray of hope for reversing this trend lies with plant propagators, however. Many of these rainforest plants exhibit complex seed dormancy and the common factor in breaking it is the journey of the seeds through the digestive tract of the animals which distribute the seed. It is well known that the stomach of most animals contains various strong acids which aid in the chemical decomposition of food. Thus, soaking seeds of these species in strong acids provides a useful starting point for propagators. It is thought that the basis for dormancy in these species lies in chemical inhibitors, either in the seed coat or within the seed. Another interesting treatment for this sort of dormancy relies on leaching out the chemical inhibitors by placing the seeds in running water. This can be done by placing the seeds in an old stocking and suspending it in running water such as in a creek or river, or another interesting alternative is in a regularly flushed toilet cistern (that's the bit at the *top* of the toilet, in case you were wondering!).

Temperature related dormancy

In areas that experience very cold winters, plant growth stops completely when the temperature drops to freezing point. In such areas the resident plants have adapted by confining their growth to the few warmer months of the year from late spring to early autumn when flowering and fruiting occurs. Seed is normally shed during late summer and early autumn. Now, imagine if this seed germinates immediately. The tender young seedling would then face the prospect of frost, or even being buried under several feet of snow! Obviously this is a very powerful natural selection pressure that has resulted in plants evolving seeds which stay dormant during the harsh winter period and then germinate and establish during the warmer months. Propagators simulate the winter conditions through a treatment known as **stratification**, which means layering the seed in a moist medium such as fine sand or peat moss and placing it into a cool room or refrigerator for several months. See table 2 Appendix 2 for details of treatments and species which respond. Such treatment even works with some Australian species that come from the alpine regions of southern New South Wales, Victoria and Tasmania.

Chemical treatments used to break dormancy

Certain chemicals including plant growth regulators (hormones) have been effective in breaking dormancy in various species.

- **Gibberellins** Perhaps the most commonly used is gibberellic acid, a plant growth regulator that stimulates growth not only in seeds but also in the growing tip of a plant. Gibberellins (gibberellic acid is often referred to as gibberellin) are sometimes used to stimulate germination in palm seed, which is rather notorious for having long germination times, often stretching into many months. Gibberellins are available from biochemical and agricultural chemical suppliers, and seeds are soaked in water solutions of concentrations from 100 to 10 000 parts per million (ppm) (0.1 to 10 grams per litre). An interesting and useful point to note is that gibberellins are able to overcome a variety of dormancy mechanisms, including the need for stratification, for light, for smoke treatment, and for after-ripening of the embryo in some species such as grasses. The obvious conclusion is that these various environmental factors trigger off the natural production of gibberellin in the seed. Therefore gibberellins can be used as a useful starting point in breaking dormancy if information is lacking on a particular species.

- **Cytokinins** This is another class of plant growth regulator that stimu-lates cell division in meristem tissue in plants. Benzyl amino purine is the most commonly used cytokinin, at concentrations between 100 and 1000 ppm (0.1 to 1 gram per litre), with the powder being dissolved in a small amount of dilute hydrochloric acid and then made up to volume with water. It would appear that cytokinins are most effective in breaking dormancy where chemical inhibitors are involved in creating dormancy, such as in *Acer pseudoplatanus* (sycamore maple). Cytokinins are also sometimes used in conjunction with gibberellins.

■ **Ethylene** Another plant growth regulator, ethylene, is normally associated with promoting maturation in fruits and flowers and triggering flowering in pineapples and other bromeliads, but is also active in breaking dormancy of some seeds. Peanuts (*Arachis hypogaea*) are an example, and an elevation of ethylene levels accompanies germination. Ethylene can be generated artificially through commercially available products such as Ethephon®. This liquid is mixed with water and the seed is soaked in the solution.

■ **Other chemicals** A variety of chemicals such as plant extracts, derivatives of smoke, potassium nitrate and sulphur compounds have all been shown to have some activity in breaking dormancy in different species (see Langkamp, 1987 *Germination of Australian Native Plant Seed*).

Handling of seedlings after germination

There are numerous ways in which seedlings may be handled after germination. Obviously the aim should be to minimise disturbance to the root system when transplanting seedlings. Systems such as cell trays are designed such that seedlings can develop their own individual root system, and these represent an excellent option for mass production situations. Where seed can be sown individually directly into cell trays by means such as a vacuum seeder, the process becomes very cost-effective. Sometimes it is very difficult to sow seed individually into cells, and the seedlings must be moved from a mass planting to individual containers. The process of moving seedlings from a community container to an individual container or into the open ground is usually referred to as **pricking out**. Seeds are usually germinated in a greenhouse situation and after pricking out they are moved to a hardening-off area such as a shadehouse before they are planted into their final position.

For seedlings that have a shallow root system that is likely to be short-lived, such as with annuals and herbaceous perennials, cell trays probably repre-

Seedlings should be transplanted into suitable containers as soon as they are big enough to handle.

sent the most cost-effective option for pricking out. The cell trays are filled with a suitable potting mix and the seedlings are dibbled individually into the cells. As mentioned earlier in this chapter, commercial production of seedlings often involves seed being sown directly into cell trays thereby eliminating the need for the costly pricking out process.

For seedlings of trees and shrubs that have much longer life spans, much greater attention should be paid to the root development of the seedling after pricking out. Much damage can be done to the root systems of these plants in the first few months of their lives and it can often be irretrievable. The biggest problem with trees and shrubs is pricking them out into standard round pots that have the normal system of drainage holes at the base of the pot. Basically the roots grow to the sides and bottom of the pot and when they hit these, the roots continue to grow and curl around the inside of the pot. When the plant eventually goes in the ground the roots will start to grow out from this curled root ball, but as they do, the original roots expand in diameter and eventually start to strangle each other in a process known as **root girdling**. The end result is that the plant is weakly anchored in the ground and is likely to topple over at some stage of its development. It will also be much more prone to root diseases and other stresses.

Root curling and girdling in tree and shrub seedlings can be greatly reduced by pricking out seedlings into special pots that are designed to stop the damage. Special extra long tubes (commonly known as tree or forestry tubes) are available, and provide a great deal of extra potting mix for root development. In addition, containers designed for this purpose will often have either hollow bottoms or minimal amounts of support at the bottom so that when the roots reach the bottom of the container they essentially hit thin air. Instead of continuing to grow and curl around the bottom of the pot, the root tip dies when it hits the air, and this results in it branching out in much the same way that a shoot does if it is tip pruned. This process is known as **air pruning of roots**. In addition, many of these special containers also have tiny ribs moulded onto the inside of the pot walls running from top to bottom. These ribs channel any roots that reach the side wall of the pot in a downwards direction, and when they reach the bottom of the pot they are air pruned.

Tips

One of the problems in dealing with tiny seedlings is that they are so fragile. Careless handling can easily lead to damage to the stem and/or roots that can mean death or permanent damage to the seedling. The safest way to hold a seedling when it is being replanted is by the leaves. If a leaf is bruised or broken the plant will usually recover. However, if the stem is handled roughly it may mean the end of the plant.

Finally, whatever type of container is used for seedlings, it is critical that the plants are not left in these containers for too long. As soon as several roots have reached the bottom of the container and the root ball holds together when removed from the container, the plant is ready to be moved. Any delay at this point will result in the plant being stunted and in many cases it will never reach its full potential.

The bird of paradise *(Strelitzia reginae)* is readily propagated by seed. A small nick should be made in the seed coat to help break dormancy. *Melinda Bargwanna*

CHAPTER 4

Stem Cuttings

Apart from seed, stem cuttings are perhaps the easiest way to propagate large numbers of plants rapidly. In fact, there are many plants that can be easily struck by placing the base of the cuttings in a glass of water—what could be simpler! And of course stem cuttings are a vegetative method of propagation, meaning that they will all be identical to the parent plant—something that cannot always be guaranteed with seed. There are several different types of stem cuttings that can be described according to the degree of woodiness of the stem (a function of the various stages of the annual growth cycle of a woody plant). The three types normally distinguished are softwood, semi-hardwood and hardwood, with the names being wonderfully self-explanatory. There are some species, such as impatiens or tomatoes, that never develop woody stems (they are known as herbaceous plants), and obviously for these plants the only type

All these classic Australian plants are easily propagated by seed. Bottom, Wattle and flame pea both need boiling water treatment to break their hard coats. Top, Kangaroo paw and flannel flower on the other hand respond to smoke treatment. *Melinda Bargwanna* of cutting material available is soft wood. But for trees and shrubs, where the stems become woody through the development of lignin tissue in the stem, all three types of wood are available to the propagator at different stages of the growing season.

It is important to recognise that all three stages of shoot development may be present on the one plant at a particular time. For instance, if we look at a shrub in late summer, we may find soft, succulent new growth at the top of the canopy, while the bottom branches may have ceased growth and be at either the semi-hardwood or hardwood stage. It is therefore vitally important that you come to recognize the various growth stages so that the best cutting material can be selected.

The physical characteristics of each type of cutting are listed below:

Softwood
Stem colour usually light green or red.
No terminal bud is visible, only newly expanding leaves.
Stem usually snaps cleanly when bent and is very sappy inside.

Semi-hardwood
Stem colour darker green but not usually brown.
Newest leaves fully expanded and a terminal bud is visible.
Stem does not snap cleanly when bent and is not sappy inside.

Hardwood
Stem colour usually brown
Newest leaves fully expanded and a terminal bud is visible. Leaves may be absent in deciduous plants.
Stem does not snap cleanly when bent and is not sappy inside.

Getting started with stem cuttings

- **Medium:** A fairly open mix is required to give excellent drainage and aeration around the base of the cutting. Various ingredients can provide the coarse particle size necessary for good aeration. Coarse washed river sand, perlite, coarse ash and composted pine bark fines are all used successfully by commercial propagators. Fifty to 75 per cent of these coarse particles mixed with an ingredient such as well rotted compost, processed coconut fibre ('cocopeat') or peat moss will generally give good results. Higher proportions of coarse particles are recommended in situations where the medium will be kept moist by a misting system or a humidity tent.

- **Container:** Pots of virtually any size are suitable, but it is better if they not too deep (say no deeper than 10 centimetres), as the cutting is usually destined for repotting into a bigger container or into the ground as soon as it forms roots. Species with fine or brittle root systems (grevilleas, for instance) should be done in individual containers of say 2.5 to 5 centimetres in diameter. This will mean minimal damage to the roots on transplanting.

- **Method:** For most stem cuttings, the tip of the stem will generally make the best cutting. If material is scarce it is usually possible to use material further back from the tip, although this may result in slower and lower rates of rooting as well as a variable type of cutting. The length of the cutting will depend on the size of the internode (the part of the stem between each leaf base). Where the internodes are very close together, cuttings can be as short as 2–3 centimetres. However, for long internodes the cutting should contain at least three nodes (the part where the leaf meets the stem) and this will determine how long the cutting is. For instance, if the internode is 5 centimetres long the cutting will need to be at least 15 centimetres long. For very short internodes, say a millimetre, the cutting need only be as long as makes it easy to handle. For many species root formation is best at the nodes (and for some species only at the nodes), and so when preparing the cutting the base is usually made just below a node. If the shoot tip has been removed for any reason, the top of the cutting should be made just above a node.

Generally between a third and two-thirds of the leaves are removed. Greater amounts are removed if the cutting is likely to be subjected to moisture stress such as an extreme summer's day. I prefer not to cut leaves in half as is sometimes seen for larger leafed species, but rather to remove a greater quantity of whole leaves. Halved leaves, in my experience, provide greater surface area for the potential entry of disease-causing organisms. Halving the leaves can sometimes be useful where there is considerable overlap of leaves in the pot, something that can lead to rotting of leaves. For semi-hardwood and hardwood cuttings, root formation can be enhanced by taking a thin sliver of bark off at the base of the cutting to a length of about a centimetre. This is known as wounding, with the idea being that immediately below the bark lies the vascular tissue where the adventitious roots will form; exposing an extra area of it gives greater surface area for root formation. Further enhancement can be gained by dipping the base of the cutting into a root promoting hormone (auxin). Auxins can be delivered either as a powder, liquid or gel and the strength is varied for different types of wood—the harder the wood, the higher the auxin concentration. Commercial hormone preparations usually specify the type of cutting to which they are best suited. Generally 1000–2000 ppm (parts per million) of an auxin such as indole butyric acid (IBA) is used for softwood cuttings, 3000–5000 ppm for semi-hardwood and up to 15 000 ppm for hardwood cuttings. A much more detailed coverage on the theory of auxins, wounding and other aspects of adventitious root formation is given later in this chapter.

- **Propagation environment:** This is a crucial factor, particularly with softwood cuttings. The softer the cutting, the greater the degree of environmental control necessary. Misting or fogging is highly desirable for leafy, soft material in commercial situations. An upended drink bottle can be used as a mini greenhouse in the home garden. Hardwood cuttings of deciduous species are usually struck towards the end of winter, while the plant is still leafless. They can be quite successfully struck outdoors in a well-drained medium (which could even be garden soil)—grapes are a good example of plants that can be done this way. Semi-hardwood and evergreen hardwood cuttings have foliage, but it is fully formed and much more resistant to wilting than the tender foliage of a softwood cutting.

- **Time of year:** This varies with the different cutting types—the time of year often dictates what type of wood will be available. Softwood material is available in spring at the beginning of the growing season, but may also be available throughout the warmer months of the year, particularly if we encourage it by tip pruning, fertilizing and watering the plant. Semi-hardwood material is available in mid-summer and autumn as the strengthening of the stem begins, while the hardwood material is available at the end of the season, in late autumn through to winter. Having given these general guidelines, it is important to say that there are no hard and fast rules about timing, as local weather patterns will dictate the growth of outdoor trees and shrubs and, of course, we can manipulate growth patterns by growing our stock plants in protected environments.

■ **Things to look for in the stock plant:** The quality of the stock plant has an enormous influence on the success rate of stem cuttings. Generally speaking, the stock plant should be grown under ideal conditions with respect to light, water and fertilizer levels. Garden specimens that are competing with other plants will make poor stock plants, as the stems produced are usually spindly and lacking in stored food, and are often infested with pests and diseases. Look for plump, healthy stems that have obviously been the result of vigorous vegetative growth. Another thing to look for is the juvenile growth that is often formed on woody plants that have been cut back very hard and is most likely to be found close to the base of the plant. This juvenile growth, which generally has leaves that are a different shape to the normal adult foliage, is very vigorous and strikes roots much more readily.

Theory of Stem Cuttings

Growing plants from stem cuttings is perhaps the method of vegetative propagation which most home gardeners and horticulturists will be familiar with. It works readily with a very wide range of species and can be used to rapidly multiply plants which are amenable to this method. Let us look in detail at the three types of stem cuttings—softwood, semi-hardwood and hardwood. To fully understand the different types and when each type is applicable, we must look at the development of a typical woody plant stem.

Most woody plants commence their annual growth cycle as the weather warms in spring, and you are no doubt familiar with the soft, sappy growth which characterises spring growth. Growth occurs mainly in the tip where the cells are dividing rapidly and are adding to the length of the shoot (this is termed **primary growth**). As spring progresses into summer, cell division starts to slow in the shoot tip and picks up further back on the stem in the vascular cambium (the tissue which divides to give rise to the xylem and phloem on the outside of the stem). Phloem and xylem tissues conduct food and water respectively, and ultimately thicken to become the dead heart-wood which adds to the thickness of the stem each year. So as the growing season progresses, the stem starts to become woody, and between mid-summer and autumn it reaches the **semi-hardwood** stage where the stem is starting to change colour and tip growth has ceased completely, but thickening of the stem is still occurring. Towards the end of autumn and into winter almost all cell division ceases within the stem. Then the **hardwood** stage is reached and the shoot has reached its dormant period. Obviously there are many plants which do not develop woody stems—these are described as herbaceous, and will only ever develop softwood.

As a general rule, the softer the wood, the better and quicker will be the chance of root formation. For any given species it is usually possible to take cuttings at each stage mentioned above. However, the harder the wood, the longer it takes for the cutting to strike. On the other side of the coin, though, the harder the wood, the less chance there is of water stress, thus lowering the requirement for humidity control in the propagation environment. In other words, hardwood cuttings tend to be much more tolerant of variations in temperature and humidity due to the fact that they are fully hardened off before they are taken. Let us now look in a little more detail at each type of cutting.

Softwood cuttings

We are all familiar with the sappy, succulent new growth which gives spring its fresh, bright green impression. So the features to look for in selecting softwood material are:

- Bright coloured stem, usually light green but may be red or purple in some species.
- The stem snaps cleanly when it is bent backwards.
- The shoot tip is still actively growing, with small unexpanded leaves clearly visible.

When looking at woody plants in general, this type of growth is very useful for the production of cuttings, as its physiological state allows for easier root formation. There are a number of reasons for this. Firstly, when a shoot is elongating rapidly, the growing tip is producing much greater quantities of a group of growth regulating substances or hormones known as **auxins**. Auxins are able to stimulate the formation of adventitious roots and if insufficient natural levels occur in the shoot, artificial auxin treatments can be applied to the base of cuttings. If auxin treatments are used for softwood cuttings they are generally applied at low concentrations of around 1000 ppm of active ingredient (usually indole butyric acid—IBA, or naphthalene acetic acid—NAA). (The topic of auxins is covered in greater detail later in this chapter and in Chapter 13.) So from the point of view of

Many softwood cuttings can be easily propagated by standing them in a jar of water. Australian plants such as Brachycome (top, bottom right), Scaevola and Myoporum (bottom left) are pictured here.

cutting production, the synthesis of auxins in the shoot tip is a real bonus, as it often reduces or eliminates the need to apply synthetic auxins. Secondly, as the growing season progresses, the shoots in a woody plant start to strengthen due to the production of lignins and other chemicals which not only reinforce the stems but also tend to make it more difficult for new roots to emerge through the stem.

Softwood cuttings are the most difficult to handle because of the very soft shoot tip they possess. This means that far more stringent environmental controls are necessary while the cuttings are being prepared and after they have been planted. Various devices can be used to help in the handling of soft cuttings, but the key thing to remember is that they should be taken when the shoots are fully turgid (i.e. the cells are full of water) and then maintained at very high humidity until they have struck roots. Placing cuttings in a plastic bag in a cool shady place (preferably a refrigerator) and squirting in a little water will greatly assist in keeping the cuttings fresh. Chapter 12, Environmental Control, details the various ways of achieving a suitable propagation environment.

Semi-hardwood cuttings

Observe some of your favourite trees and shrubs (such as camellias or callistemons) in the garden as growth progresses during spring and summer. Depending on how much water and nutrients the plants are receiving, at some point you will notice that the shoot tip stops producing new leaves and the leaves at the tip become fully expanded. At this point the stem has ceased primary growth (and has stopped lengthening) but is still undergoing secondary growth (i.e. thickening of the stem) and is at an ideal stage for semi-hardwood cuttings. The signs to look for then are:

■ The stem is changing colour, usually from bright green to brown.
■ The stem does not snap cleanly.
■ The uppermost leaves are fully expanded and often a terminal bud is
   present.

Semi-hardwood cuttings are used for species in which softwood growth is extremely tender and wilts too easily for softwood cuttings to be used. This wilting often leads to fungal infections and rotting out of the cutting. Semi-hardwoods, on the other hand, are much tougher and are self-supporting because of the woodiness of the stem. They also do not need as much humidity and give the propagator much greater room to move as far as controlling the propagation environment is concerned. Therefore, there are still many trees and shrubs where semi-hardwood cuttings are preferred to softwood. Semi-hardwood cuttings can also be stored more readily than softwood cuttings.

On the other hand, semi-hardwood cuttings tend to take much longer to strike than softwoods, say months rather than weeks. This is no doubt because metabolic activity has slowed down in the stem, and there is also much less auxin being produced naturally in the shoot tip. Accordingly, semi-hardwoods often benefit greatly from auxin treatments applied to the base of the cutting and at much higher concentrations than for softwood cuttings. Anything from 3000–8000 ppm of active ingredient (usually IBA or NAA) is used (in extraordinary cases up to 15 000 ppm may be used). For more detail, see the section later in this chapter on auxin treatments. Wounding of the base of the stem and bottom heating of cuttings are other useful treatments that will be covered later in this chapter.

Semi-hardwood cuttings work best with evergreen plants, as deciduous species will drop their leaves during winter and this will create a carpet of dead leaves around the base of the cutting. These decaying leaves will often encourage diseases such as botrytis (grey mould). It is possible to strike deciduous semi-hardwood cuttings before they lose their leaves for some species that mature early in the season. The cuttings can then be over-wintered as leafless cuttings to be potted up in spring, but this means removing the fallen leaves, which can be time consuming.

Hardwood cuttings

In most climates, as a tree or shrub moves from summer to winter, growth will cease entirely and the plant enters dormancy—primary and secondary growth have ceased altogether. Because of this very dormant condition, hardwood cuttings are the most resilient of the three types and are very useful in situations where the propagator has minimal control over the propagation environment. In fact, many deciduous species can be done in outdoor beds as leafless hardwood cuttings that will strike in spring. The things to look for in hardwood cuttings are:

■ The stem is usually brown or dark in colour.

- The stem does not snap cleanly when bent.
- For deciduous species, cuttings need to be taken after leaf fall in autumn.
- The stem tip will have a terminal bud present.

Hardwood cuttings tend to be used infrequently in commercial operations these days because they take much longer to strike than the other cutting types. However, they are still very useful for propagators such as home gardeners who have minimal facilities. Another advantage is that they are usually taken in winter when there are very few other propagation tasks to be done.

Some specialized commercial applications, such as the outdoor production of budded roses, remain for hardwood cuttings. In this situation hardwood cuttings of the rose rootstock are taken and planted in rows in the field in late winter, and the struck cuttings are then budded in summer or autumn and dug for sale in the following year. Auxin treatments are generally beneficial for hardwood cuttings, and these are applied at high levels of 10 000 ppm or greater of active ingredient (usually IBA or NAA). Wounding is also useful, and both these topics are covered in more detail later in this chapter. Hardwood cuttings need lower levels of humidity and can often be struck outdoors, especially if they are deciduous species.

Storage of stem cuttings

All three types of cuttings can be readily stored, but obviously the softer the growth, the more fragile the cuttings are and the less time they can be successfully stored. Softwood and semi-hardwood cuttings should be wrapped in damp newspaper and put into a plastic bag which is then placed in a refrigerator at as low a temperature as possible, down to 3 degrees Celsius. In places with harsh winter climates, leafless hardwood cuttings of deciduous woody plants are sometimes stored in **callus boxes**. Bundles of twenty or so cuttings are layered in slightly moist peat moss in a shallow box and stored in a cool but not freezing environment. The cuttings are stored in the callus box until spring when they are planted out in prepared—usually raised—outdoor beds. Stored cuttings of all types should be inspected every week or so to ensure they are not infected with any pathogens. If they are, an appropriate remedial treatment such as a fungicide should be applied.

Difficult to Root Cuttings— Tricks of the Trade

Root promoting compounds and techniques

1. **Auxins** are a group of hormones that regulate a multitude of growth and development processes in plants. As propagators, our primary interest is in their ability to stimulate adventitious root formation in cuttings. The most common naturally occurring auxin is indole acetic acid (IAA), which is synthesised in the shoot tip and transported back down the plant via the phloem. Unfortunately IAA is unstable in light and therefore of limited use for artificial application to cuttings. A range of synthetically produced auxins is available and these are much more stable and very effective for the propagator's purposes. Indole butyric acid (IBA) and naphthalene acetic acid (NAA) are the most commonly used for application to cuttings. They are used at concentrations ranging from 1000 to 50 000 parts per million (ppm).

   Auxins can be applied to cuttings in a variety of ways. Perhaps the most common but not necessarily most effective method is as a powder in which the minute quantity of auxin required is mixed thoroughly with a much larger volume of talcum powder. These powders are commonly available commercially in a wide range of concentrations. The other commonly available auxin preparation is a sticky gel into which the base of the cutting is dipped. Such auxin gels are often supplemented with additives such as vitamins like thiamine and mineral nutrients such as nitrogen, potassium and other essential elements for plant growth. Auxins can also be made up as water solutions to be used for dipping or soaking the base of cuttings. In this case the auxin powder is dissolved in as small an amount of alcohol as possible and then made up to the appropriate volume with water. This technique allows the propagator to make up whatever auxin concentration he or she desires. In all cases, lower levels such as 1000 ppm are generally recommended for softwood cuttings, intermediate levels (3000–8000 ppm) for semi-hardwood cuttings and high levels (10 000 ppm and over) for hardwoods. Auxin solutions, whether they be aqueous solutions or gels, can be applied either as a quick dip (say for 5 seconds) or as a soak for a period of hours. The best advice I can give on the use of auxins is that the response varies widely from species to species and there is no substitute for researching the requirements on an individual basis. Therefore, the propagator should test each species under his or her own conditions with a variety of auxin treatments. Obviously such testing will be much more useful where very large numbers of cuttings are being done. A practical example is the production of chrysanthemum cuttings, which strike very readily with or without auxins. In this case, dispensing with the auxin treatment results in a delay of maybe a couple of days in the time to root formation, but there is significant saving in the time it takes to prepare the cutting and in not using the reasonably expensive hormone preparation.

2. **Vitamins** The evidence that vitamins such as thiamine and riboflavin play a part in adventitious root formation comes largely from tissue culture research in which plants are grown on highly controlled sterile nutrient media. Thiamine, riboflavin, pyridoxine, ascorbic acid and nicotinic acid have been shown to be beneficial to root formation in a number of species (See further Hartmann and Kester, *Plant Propagation*). These complex organic substances are thought to play a role in speeding up the rate of biochemical reactions in the plant. Some commercially available auxin gels are made up to include vitamins. The fact that most cutting propagation is done quite satisfactorily without added vitamins suggests that there must either be sufficient levels in the cutting naturally, or that vitamins are desirable but not essential for root formation. Once again, it may be that such factors are useful for especially difficult to root species.

3. **Mineral nutrients** Nitrogen in particular has a stimulatory effect on rooting of cuttings of some species, and this is perhaps not surprising given the general positive response of plant growth to nitrogen when it is applied as a fertiliser. It is thought that as well as acting as a nutrient, nitrogen may also interact with auxins and enhance their activity. Boron has also been shown to enhance root formation in a range of species, particularly when used in conjunction with IBA (See further Hartmann and Kester, *Plant Propagation*).

4. **Fungicides** There have been suggestions over the years that some fungicides have a stimulatory effect on root formation over and above that caused by suppression of fungal pathogens. Obviously, if a pathogenic fungus is attacking cuttings, fungicides are likely to have a stimulatory

effect by suppressing the fungus. In many nurseries fungicides are used as a preventative treatment when cuttings are planted, just in case a pathogenic fungus is present. The obvious problem with this practice is that the fungus will sooner or later develop a resistance to the fungicide, and the propagators options for disease control will become ever more limited and expensive. It is therefore recommended that fungicides are used as a curative treatment where applicable, and if they are to be used as a preventative measure, this should only be done where there is a history of problems with a particular pathogen.

5. **Wounding** This refers to the practice of scraping a narrow strip of bark from the base of the cutting. The wound is made by using a sharp knife or razor blade to cut a sliver of bark off so that the vascular tissue underneath is exposed for a couple of centimetres at the base of the cutting. The vascular tissue is that green sappy tissue just under the bark, and it is the place where the new roots will arise. There are several benefits of wounding: it gives a greater surface area for root formation, it makes it easier for roots to emerge from the stem, and it also allows for increased water uptake by the cutting which can be vital to its survival in the early stages. The downside of wounding is that it is a labour-intensive practice, and in commercial situations is only desirable for species that are difficult to root. In the home garden, however, there is nothing to lose and everything to gain by doing whatever will improve your chances of success. For exceptionally difficult plants, multiple wounds can be made around the stem.

6. **Bottom heat** Raising the temperature of the propagation medium is a simple and very effective way of improving results with most cuttings. I would suggest that bottom heat will be far more beneficial than increasing the air temperature around the cuttings. An elevated aerial temperature without bottom heat can encourage leaf growth before root formation, something that may even cause the death of the cutting if it becomes water stressed. Bottom heating of the medium, up to a temperature of 25 degrees Celsius, will give good results in most situations. There are a number of technologies available to provide bottom heat, and the actual choice will depend on availability and running costs. In my experience the most cost-effective systems are based on pumping heated water through pipes embedded or even placed on top of the bench the cuttings are sitting

on. Usually the heating pipes or cables are covered with fine sand which should be kept slightly moist to enable most efficient transmission of the heat. The water is generally heated by off-peak electricity or gas. Self-contained propagation trays for home gardeners are available commercially and are advertised in home gardening magazines. These usually have conventional plugs that can be inserted into ordinary electricity sockets.

7. **Etiolation** Excluding or reducing the amount of light a stock plant receives has long been known to increase root formation in cuttings taken from it. This can be achieved by growing the stock plant in heavy shade under a covering of black cloth, black polyethylene or shade cloth. Whilst it was originally thought that it was necessary to exclude all light during the etiolation process, propagators have had good results by using shade levels as low as 50 per cent on both woody and herbaceous species. The etiolation treatment is generally applied for a period of two to four weeks, after which time the shoots are generally pale due to lack of chlorophyll and have longer internodes as well. Stock plants should be returned to higher light levels for a week or so before cuttings are taken in order to harden them up a little and reduce problems which may occur with fungal pathogens such as botrytis (grey mould). Examples of species which have been proven to respond to etiolation are mangoes (*Mangifera indica*), avocadoes (*Persea americana*), lilac cultivars (*Syringa vulgaris*), *Clematis* species and smoke bush (*Cotinus coggygria*).

8. **Blanching** A variation on etiolation is blanching or banding, which is the exclusion of light from a localised area of the stem which will be used as the base of the cutting. Various materials can be used to achieve blanching, including black tape, paper, tubing, aluminium foil and velcro. The band should be applied close to the shoot tip (within 2 to 3 centimetres) for optimum results. In other words, the band is applied at the start of the growing season, and the cutting is taken when the shoot has elongated, with the banded section forming the base of the cutting. The band should be roughly 5 centimetres wide, and further enhancement of results can be obtained by coating the inside of the bands with an appropriate talc preparation of auxin, usually IBA. Species where banding/blanching has been shown to be successful include *Acer platanoides*, *Tilia* species, *Pinus elliottii*, *Platanus occidentalis* and *Rhododendron* cultivars.

Yet another idea for the intrepid propagator is to use a combination of etiolation and banding to further enhance results. The idea here is to etiolate the shoots using the treatment outlined above. Once the shoots are etiolated the shading is removed and suitable young shoots are banded near the tips and then allowed to grow out under normal light conditions. This strategy has been successfully used with plants such as *Acer* species, *Betula papyrifera*, *Pinus* species, *Quercus* species (oaks), *Pistachia vera* and *Syringa vulgaris* and its cultivars (lilacs).

9. **Juvenility** Many woody plants become progressively more difficult to root as they get older. A woody plant seedling actually goes through a maturation process where it starts life in a **juvenile stage** when growth is extremely vigorous and flowering usually does not occur. The plant may then move through an **intermediate stage** and finally reach the **adult stage** when it gains full maturity and is able to produce flowers and therefore seeds. Adventitious root formation is always much easier in the juvenile stage. Therefore, for difficult to root species the use of juvenile

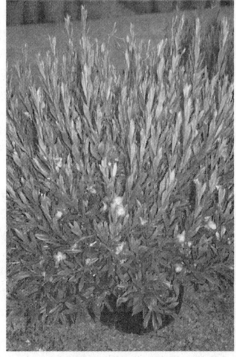

Hard pruning *Grevillea* 'Robyn Gordon' (left) and *Crowea saligna* (right) result in juvenile regrowth which makes for much higher strike rates in cutting material.

material will often lead to much higher strike rates with cuttings. Fortunately for us, stock plants of many species can be switched from adult to juvenile stage through the use of hard pruning. (See Chapter 11 on Stock Plant Management for a full discussion of this phenomenon.)

Why do etiolation and banding treatments work?

The enhancement of rooting appears to be associated with changes that take place in etiolated and banded stems such as decreased stem strength, lack of chlorophyll and increased succulence. Maynard and Bassuk (See Further Reading list) suggest that the weakened state of the stems aids in the emergence and development of roots at the base of cuttings. In addition, they suggest that a range of physiological changes also occur in the treated stem sections which enhance meristematic activity (new cell formation) and the action of naturally formed auxins within the plant.

Should fertilisers be added to media for cutting production?

This issue seems to raise a lot of controversy when it is discussed by plant propagators. Obviously when cuttings are first set they have no means of absorbing nutrients from the medium, and there is no need to add fertiliser at this stage. However, nutrients may still be absorbed through the foliage and stem, and given that there is evidence to suggest that mineral nutrients may enhance root formation in cuttings, I believe feeding will certainly do no harm. A light dose of a liquid feed such as Aquasol® could be watered onto the cuttings every week or so. As soon as root initiation occurs the liquid feeding will also be absorbed from the medium by the new roots. It is very important that cuttings which are fed in this way are potted as soon as practicable, as the high planting density of cuttings will result in very spindly growth if they are left unpotted after rooting. If it becomes necessary to hold the cuttings, then simply cease feeding. The use of slow-release fertilisers in the cutting medium is another possibility, particularly for fast rooting cuttings such as soft tip types. However, slow-release fertilisers will continue to release if the cuttings have to remain in the medium if potting is delayed for whatever reason. Thus liquid feeding offers much more flexibility in keeping the cuttings at their best, whatever happens.

All species of *Tibouchina* are readily propagated by softwood cuttings. *Melinda Bargwanna*

Root-inducing Bacteria

One of the startling breakthroughs of modern science has been genetic engineering, where genes (discrete pieces of DNA which code for particular characteristics) from one organism can be inserted into another organism. One of the most successful methods of transferring genes is employing the bacteria *Agrobacterium tumefaciens*. Normally, this bacteria causes a disease called crown gall in a wide range of plant species including, for instance, roses. The way in which it causes the gall (a tumour-like swelling at the base of the stem) is by inserting a part of its DNA into the plant's chromosomes, thereby altering the genetic message the plant cells receive, causing a cancer-like reaction and forming a gall. Genetic engineers have found a way of piggybacking other genes onto the *Agrobacterium* DNA whilst eliminating the tumour formation. The new gene/s added by the genetic engineers are then passed from generation to generation.

A little known cousin of the crown gall bacteria is *Agrobacterium rhizogenes*, a soil-living bacterium that can enter plant roots and stimulate the growth of masses of secondary roots to create a condition known as 'hairy root'. It can infect a wide range of dicotyledonous plants (i.e. plants that have two cotyledons in their seeds and have leaf veination that is not parallel, as it is in the monocotyledons). The condition caused by the bacteria does not appear to have any deleterious effects on the plant and it has thus excited interest in its possible use to encourage root formation in cuttings and other propagation methods. The rather fascinating thing about this bacteria is that, like its cousin *Agrobacterium tumefaciens*, it causes its effect on the plant by inserting part of its DNA into the chromosomes of the plant, and the bacterial DNA causes the plant to manufacture the extra roots. In effect the bacteria genetically engineers the plant to produce its effect. Researchers have attempted to use the bacteria to enhance root formation in cuttings and bare rooted stock. The results have been promising and may lead to commercial use in the future (See Strobel and Nachmias, 1988, in Further Reading list).

Bottlebrushes *(Callistemon* species*)* top right and feather flowers (Melinda Bargwanna) *(Verticordia* species*)* bottom left are both ideal candidates for semi-hardwood cuttings. Top left: Waratah *(Telopea* species*)* can be propagated from hardwood cuttings in late autumn. Bottom right: *Lechenaultia biloba* (Melinda Bargwanna) is propagated from softwood cuttings in Spring.

Summary of Adventitious Root Formation in Cuttings

Adventitious root formation is obviously a complex process involving the interaction of many factors and it is impossible to pinpoint any single factor as being of over-riding importance. However, perhaps a better way of looking at the issue is to identify all the conditions which favour adventitious root formation and try to optimise them. Each species or even cultivar may need individual variations to give best results. Stock plant management is a crucial starting point and here we can optimise nutrition, juvenility, watering and elimination of pests and diseases. The next stage is in the prepartion and setting of the cutting, where we can manipulate factors such as turgidity of foliage, wounding, auxin treatment (if applicable), blanching or etiolation and the size of cutting. The propagation environment can be optimised through careful control of bottom and aerial temperatures, humidity through misting, fogging or humidity tents, light levels through shading. Finally, the hardening off process may require the provision of a shadehouse in the initial stage to avoid stressing the cuttings unduly as they are brought out of the 'humidicrib-like' conditions of the average propagation house.

CHAPTER 5

Leaf Cuttings

Hen and
chicken fern

There is a small group of plants which has an extraordinary ability to regenerate new plantlets—they are so regenerative that they are capable of forming both shoots and roots from their leaf cells. African violets provide the classic example of plants ideally suited to this propagation method. A wonderful exercise is to take an African violet leaf with its leaf stalk (petiole) and place it in a jar of water with just the end of the petiole submerged in water. You can then watch the fascinating process of root and shoot formation at the base of the petiole. A number of other popular indoor plants such as rex begonias, cape primrose (*Streptocarpus*) and peperomias are also routinely propagated commercially by leaf cuttings.

- **Medium:** The very soft tissues that are typical of most species used for leaf cuttings mean that the cuttings are very prone to rotting by fungi and/or bacteria. Thus it is very important with leaf cuttings to not only have a medium that is well drained and well aerated, but also one that does not contain any plant pathogens. A simple solution is to use ingredients that are likely to be free of pathogens from the beginning, such as perlite (which should be sterile when it comes out of the bag) and peat moss in a 50:50 ratio. Another option is to purchase a bagged commercial propagation mix that has been pasteurised before packaging.

- **Container:** There are no special requirements for containers for leaf cuttings.
- **Method:** There are a number of variations of the actual part of the leaf that can be used and these will be given in detail later in this chapter. A quick and simple one for the home gardener is the leaf and petiole cutting. This is applicable to a number of popular house plants such as African violets (*Saintpaulia ionantha*), rex begonias (*Begonia rex*) and piggyback plant (*Tolmiea menziesii*). The leaf and petiole cutting is normally taken by detaching a whole leaf with its petiole and planting it with just the petiole submerged in the medium. In addition to using a normal potting mix, a useful trick is to fill a small jar (I swear by Vegemite jars) with water and close it off at the top with a couple of layers of aluminium foil held on by a rubber band. Small holes are then poked in the foil, and the African violet leaves 'planted' into these holes in the same way they would be in a normal medium.
- **Propagation environment:** Leaf cuttings generally consist of very soft tissue and are therefore prone to drying out, so a reasonable level of humidity must be maintained. However, too much humidity can create conditions conducive to leaf rotting fungi and bacteria. A windowsill which receives filtered sunlight and is away from draughts is ideal for small scale propagation. An open bench in a greenhouse without mist or fogging is best for larger scale work. Bottom heating is generally beneficial as well, but particular care must be exercised with watering to ensure the medium does not dry out excessively at any stage.
- **Time of year:** Most species which are propagated by leaf cuttings are those used as house plants, and thus they are normally grown in greenhouses under a reasonable degree of environmental control. Under such conditions, there is usually some growth suitable for leaf cuttings all year round.
- **Things to look for in the stock plant:** The ideal leaf cutting will be a fully expanded leaf which is in the prime of its life. Avoid leaves which are starting to yellow or have any sort of damage. Leaves should be removed from the plant with a very sharp knife or even a scalpel if available. Avoid using secateurs as these will tend to bruise the very soft succulent tissue of species propagated by leaf cuttings.

Theory of Leaf Cuttings

In general leaf cuttings are limited to soft-wooded plants, as most woody plants do not have leaves with the capacity to form adventitious shoots under normal conditions, although there are exceptions to this rule. An even more select group of plants has adopted the strategy of producing new plantlets on the leaves of established plants. When the old leaves die and drop off, the plantlets on the leaf start to root into the soil and form a new clump. Examples of this include the hen and chicken fern (*Adiantum bulbiferum*) and the piggyback plant (*Tolmiea menziesii*), both of which make excellent and novel indoor plants. Plants such as these actually have cells in the leaf, particularly in the veins, which are preprogrammed genetically to form into vegetative or 'foliar' embryos that will give rise to tiny plantlets. These fascinating structures develop in a similar way to embryos formed in developing seeds (which are the result of a union of male and female gametes from each parent), except that in this case they arise without a sexual process and are therefore known as vegetative (or somatic) embryos, and are thus identical to the parent plant. In plant species where these plantlets are preformed, they arise from what are known as **primary meristems**.

Hen and Chicken Fern

The hen and chicken fern is found in the subtropical rainforests of eastern Australia where it sometimes forms a carpet on the forest floor. It is a shade-loving plant which has a clumping habit, with fronds emerging from a central point at ground level. As the plant grows, the new fronds gradually push the older ones outwards. Eventually they lay down on the ground, and the preformed plantlets on the frond begin to grow and eventually detach form the parent plant and become independent. Over many years the colony spreads over a large area of the forest floor.

In addition to plants such as the hen and chicken fern, there is a group of plants such as African violets which have the capacity to form plantlets on the leaves, but only when the leaf is wounded and detached from the plant. In this case the new plantlet arises from the vascular tissue in the leaf veins, but not from preformed embryos. The vascular tissue must first differentiate into new shoot structures. To encourage this, we must detach the leaf from the plant, expose the veins and place the cutting into a suitable medium. The plantlets that form on the leaf in this case arise from **secondary meristems,** since they are not preformed. Understanding that these secondary embryos form most easily in and around the leaf veins helps the propagator to take best advantage of the leaf material available. By wounding (physically damaging) the veins, the propagator will produce many more sites at which new plantlets will form. Secondary meristems can also arise from callus tissue, which forms along cut surfaces.

There are a number of different ways of preparing leaf cuttings which, of course, all rely on the principal of cutting through and exposing vascular (vein) tissue to the medium. One of the major drawbacks to leaf cuttings, however, is related to this wounding process—the very soft tissue that is exposed can, under conducive conditions, be highly susceptible to fungal and bacterial rots. These conditions occur when cuttings are kept too wet or when hygiene is poor, allowing plant pathogens to fester away at the plant material. The key, then, to successful leaf cuttings is providing optimal environmental conditions and a very high level of cleanliness and hygiene. The ultimate in leaf cuttings is perhaps when leaf tissue is used in micro-propagation. Even the tiniest fragment of leaf tissue of suitable species (such as African violet) is able to regenerate as the sterile environment in the test tube means that diseases are totally excluded. Let us now look at some of the variations on the leaf cutting.

Leaf and petiole method

The leaf and petiole method of leaf cuttings is perhaps the most widely practised commercially and was detailed at the start of this chapter. New plantlets are formed at the base of the petiole, with the original leaf blade providing a source of nourishment for the whole process. The petiole and the point at which it meets the leaf blade are both very important sites for adventitious shoot formation as this is where a very high concentration of vascular tissue is found. The vascular tissue is, of course, the site where new shoots are formed. The original leaf blade eventually rots away and does not form part of the new plant. This is the classic method used for commercial African violet propagation.

Leaf section method

Another useful method, particularly where the leaf has a large surface area, is to simply cut the leaf up into sections, with each section containing at least one large piece of vein. Examples of species which suit this method include various begonias such as *Begonia rex* and *Sansevieria* (sometimes known by the controversial common name of mother-in-law's tongue). The section is then planted with the exposed vein in contact with the medium. The sections can be cut into whatever shape will give the most efficient use of space in the container. Some propagators recommend leaving the whole leaf blade intact and making small nicks across the veins, and then laying the leaf flat on the surface of the medium, weighing it down with stones or pegging it down with pieces of wire. In my experience this method is a very inefficient use of space and often results in excessive damage to the leaf tissue, which increases the risk of rotting. Cutting the leaf into wedge-shaped sections and planting them upright (take care not to plant them upside down) will give a much higher yield of plantlets for a given area. When the leaf segment method is used, a simple way of ensuring that the correct polarity is maintained is to cut the top (distal) end of the cutting at a 45 degree angle and the bottom (proximal) end at a 90 degree angle. This method is only warranted if there is a danger of planting the segments upside down as in the case of the long, thin strap-like leaves of the *Sansevieria*. Given the high expense of maintaining the average commercial propagation facility, the propagator must always strive to maximise the yield per unit area and the leaf segment method is one of the best ways of ensuring this.

Severed vein method

Plants with long, slender leaves with a prominent mid-vein such as the cape primrose (*Streptocarpus*) lend themselves to yet another variation where the leaf is sliced into two halves by running a knife immediately along either side of the mid-vein. This then exposes the base of every vein running in the leaf tissue at the point where it connects with the mid-vein. The long sections thus created are planted with the exposed veins buried in the medium. A clump of plantlets forms at every vein, resulting in a long line of plantlets which is then easily split into separate sections and potted up into individual containers when they are large enough.

General Hints on Leaf Cuttings

Using root promoting auxin treatments is a good idea. If using a ready mixed type, then select the one formulated for softwood cuttings, as it will have a relatively low concentration of auxins (usually around the 1000 ppm mark).

Other points to watch:

■ select fully expanded leaves that are in their prime and show no signs of pests or diseases
■ use chopping boards, knives or scalpels which can be regularly rinsed and sterilised in a weak solution of disinfectant
■ use a free draining, well-aerated medium which has been pasteurised or made from ingredients which are likely to be disease free, such as perlite and vermiculite
■ since most species propagated by leaf cuttings are normally used as indoor plants, they are grown in a controlled environment such as a greenhouse and can usually be struck at any time of the year as they are not as subject to seasonal growth patterns as plants grown outdoors.

CHAPTER 6

Root Cuttings

A relatively small group of plants has the ability to form a new (adventitious) shoot system directly on the roots, particularly if the roots have been wounded to the depth of the vascular tissue. The capacity of a particular plant species to sucker from the root system in a garden situation will be a very useful indicator as to whether that plant will be successfully propagated by root cuttings. In the wild, the ability to sucker provides an alternative means of surviving environmental catastrophes or grazing by animals, so that if a tree blows over, or if a fire destroys the top of a plant, the food stored in the roots can fuel the regeneration process. Rapid regeneration from the root system also means that the plant's place in the canopy is not lost. The ability to sucker from the roots appears to be fairly evenly spread between woody and herbaceous plants.

Sucker for a Shrub

There are a number of species that will sucker from the root system and develop into rather dense thickets. This can be a two-edged sword, depending on the situation. In many cases a suckering species, such as the beautiful blue plumbago, will spread and grow so thickly that it chokes out any weeds that dare to try to invade its patch. On the other hand, however, such species can themselves be rather invasive, effectively turning them into weeds—let the planter beware! Other species in this category include *Wisteria*, *Chaenomeles japonica* and *Prunus glandulosa*. There are several important tree species that also fit into this category and are therefore easily propagated by root cuttings. These include *Liquidambar styraciflua*, various poplars (*Populus* species) and *Pyrus calleryana*.

■ **Medium:** Root cuttings are not as demanding as other sorts of cuttings as they tend to have a tough exterior which resists water loss and entry of disease-causing organisms. In addition, root cuttings have no leaves through which moisture can be lost. Most general purpose potting mixes will be quite adequate for root cuttings.

- **Container:** There are no special requirements as far as containers go.

- **Method:** A garden fork is the best tool to lift the stock plant (unless it is in a pot), as it leaves more roots intact than digging with a spade. The root system is then hosed off to remove as much of the old medium as possible. Sections of root 2.5 to 5 centimetres in length are cut, and the simplest way to deal with them is to lay them horizontally on the medium and then make sure they are just covered with medium. Generally speaking, the fatter the root, the greater the amount of food stored in it, and the greater the success rate. However, for some species, such as the Japanese windflower (*Anemone* x hybrida), even the thinnest of roots are capable of sprouting. A variation of the method for larger scale propagation is to prepare the cuttings and bundle ten to 15 together with a rubber band and plant them upright in the medium, making sure that the polarity of the root is maintained (in other words the roots should be oriented the same way they were on the parent plant—if planted upside down the cutting may fail). When the cuttings have struck, the rubber band is removed and they are potted individually. Hormone treatments are generally not necessary for successful root cuttings.

- **Propagation environment:** As the cuttings have no leaves and a well developed cuticle ('skin'), no special environmental control is necessary and, provided a well drained soil is available, an outdoor garden situation will often give satisfactory results.

- **Time of year:** The optimum time is just before the plant is entering a growth phase, which is spring for most species. Often the plants suitable for root cuttings are those which can also be propagated by division, and the two events can be carried out simultaneously.

- **Things to look for in the stock plant:** A normal healthy plant, free of pests and diseases and preferably one that is looking a bit overgrown and in need of rejuvenation.

Theory of Root Cuttings

As with many other propagation methods, the success of the process depends on the cutting having a good store of nutrients to fuel the growth process. Accordingly, a stock plant which is being used for root cuttings can be managed to ensure that a greater proportion of nutrients from the plant is directed to the root system during the growing season. For ornamental species, the removal of flowers will mean that a tremendous amount of the plant's resources will be directed into vegetative growth, both in the shoot and root system. If flowering cannot be sacrificed, then at least make sure that spent flower heads are removed before any fruits are formed, as seed formation is a further drain on the plant's resources at the expense of vegetative growth. A drench of an auxin solution (say 1000 parts per million IBA) around the roots at the start of the growing season will also encourage root growth.

It is also important that the plant is in the optimum physiological state for adventitious shoot formation. Usually the optimum time to take root cuttings to ensure this state is at the beginning of the plant's annual growth cycle. For most plant species, this is the end of winter just before the spring growth surge. If the plant is going into a dormant or semi-dormant phase then the cutting is likely to go through a long period of inactivity when it may rot. This is especially so if the cuttings are going to be planted outdoors.

An interesting aspect of root cuttings is that we are trying to induce the formation of adventitious shoots. To assist this process, the group of plant hormones known as cytokinins can be used. Cytokinins are commonly added to plant tissue culture media to induce multiple shoot formation, so it is no surprise that they are also effective in stimulating shoots in root cuttings. Solutions of cytokinins can be obtained from a plant tissue culture laboratory, or alternatively solutions can be ordered from and made up by a specialist supplier of biochemicals. The powder is dissolved in a small quantity of dilute hydrochloric acid and then topped up to the required volume with water. Rates of around 0.1 ppm kinetin have been reported as effective, although I would suggest trying higher concentrations as a trial with each species.

The pattern of development in root cuttings varies from species to species, with some producing shoots before new roots, and vice versa. For older,

The Japanese windflower *(Anemone* x hybrida*)* is readily propagated from even very fine roots.

thicker roots, the formation of adventitious roots as well as shoots may be necessary. Often the new root system is produced at the base of the new shoot, and eventually the original root piece withers and dies, leaving the new vigorous plant with its own root system. Root cuttings tend to be more successful when taken from young, vigorous plants, a fact which probably reflects the 'juvenility factor' (discussed in Chapter 11).

A word of warning on root cuttings. Some types of plants, such as variegated ones, may not be genetically stable when propagated by this method. This is due to the fact that there is a rather complicated genetic basis for variegation in many species. For such plants, stem cuttings or division are often the only methods that will preserve the genetic integrity of the new plants (in other words, ensure that they are true to type).

In short, root cuttings can be a very useful method for plants that are particularly prolific at suckering, such as the Japanese windflower. It is also a very useful method if propagation is to be done outdoors with no environmental control.

CHAPTER 7

Layering

To put it simply, layering is like taking a stem cutting of a plant, except that we leave the cutting on the plant! Because the 'cutting' is left on the plant it is still connected to the parent plant's xylem, ensuring that it continues to receive water and mineral nutrition. Thus the 'cutting' can go on indefinitely until such time as the new root system forms. This makes layering an ideal method for propagating plants where cuttings are difficult to strike, and it is also a great method for the propagator who does not have access to sophisticated environmental controls such as misting or fogging systems—the parent plant does the job of nursing the new plant through! Another advantage of layering is that it is possible to produce relatively large plants, again because the parent plant is able to nurse the layer through the stressful period when roots are forming.

Layering an Old Friend

Layering is an excellent way of perpetuating a shrub or tree that has great sentimental value to a gardener. A classic example is the camellia, which will live for hundreds of years and become a large tree if allowed to. Often a large specimen planted by a previous generation of gardener is too big to be transplanted when a family moves house and leaves a dearly loved old garden behind. In such cases, layering is a fantastic way of propagating a large plant to establish at the next location. It will be successful with virtually any tree or shrub that can be propagated by cuttings.

- **Medium:** A loose, well-aerated medium is ideal for layering. Because the layer is still attached to the mother plant while a new root system is forming, the layer is still deriving water from the mother plant, and so does not need to get it from the medium. A high degree of aeration will certainly enhance root formation, so coarse materials such as composted sawdust, coconut fibre ('cocopeat') or sphagnum peat moss are ideal media for layering. A good quality general purpose potting mix will also do a reasonable job if the other materials are not available.

- **Container:** For most types of layering there is no container as such (see details later in this chapter). For aerial layering, however, the layer is suspended in mid air and the medium is enclosed in either heavy black plastic or heavy duty aluminium foil, or even a combination of both. Another useful tip is to use compressed peat pots (sold commercially under brand names such as Jiffy-pot) for the medium. These are blocks of compressed peat moss that are in a coarse netting. When they are soaked in water, the compressed peat absorbs moisture and swells dramatically to form a small plug of moist peat. A slice is then made along the plug to allow it to encircle the wounded stem. The whole thing is then wrapped in aluminium foil or plastic.

- **Method:** The two easiest and most commonly used methods of layering are simple and aerial layering. **Simple layering**—a branch close to ground level that can be bent to soil level is selected. A hole perhaps 10 centimetres deep is dug, and the shoot is bent down so that 15 centimetres or so behind the shoot tip will be buried when the hole is backfilled. The shoot tip is bent up so that it protrudes above the surface. Various treatments can be used on the buried part of the stem to encourage root

A very successful aerial layer of *Banksia* 'Giant Candles'. It is now ready to pot up. *Melinda Bargwanna*

formation. The simplest of these is to make a longitudinal slice along the stem, about a centimetre long and going just under the bark. Wedge a match or twig into the cut to keep it open, as this exposes the vascular tissue where the new root system will form. An auxin treatment can also be applied at this stage, with a gel being perhaps the best option to ensure an even coverage. The stem is then held in place while the hole is backfilled with whatever medium you have chosen (see above for choices). It is possible to get away with just using soil to backfill, provided it is reasonably friable. Once there is obvious new growth on the exposed tip it is normally the case that the layer has rooted and can be cut from the stem and potted up or transplanted to a new location. A great alternative to digging a hole and burying the shoot tip in the soil is to use a pot filled with a good quality potting mix instead. When roots appear through the drainage holes in the pot, the layer is ready to detach from the parent plant. The only drawback with this method is that the medium is more prone to drying out and will need to be hand watered from time to time for comparable results.

Aerial layering—this method is also known as **marcottage** and involves the layer being suspended in mid-air. A good way of selecting the section to be layered is to imagine how it will look in a pot or in the ground after it has rooted and been removed from the mother plant. One particular advantage of aerial layering is that the section can be as large as you like (within reason), allowing you to create a large plant that will give an instant effect when it is transplanted into the ground. Select an area on the stem that is free of any substantial side shoots. It can then be given one of the treatments which are mentioned later in the chapter, but in my experience the most effective is a technique called girdling. This involves using a sharp knife (preferably a budding or grafting knife) to cut two rings right around the stem until you are just through the bark. In most plants you will actually hear a little clicking noise as you get through the bark and reach the wood. The two rings are made 3–4 centimetres apart on the stem, and a cut is made between them, joining them up. The bark between the two rings is then lifted off completely and removed, thus creating the 'girdle' on the stem. The process of girdling is very time-consuming if it is done very neatly by using a budding knife. Where speed is more an issue, a pair of pliers can be used. The pliers are clamped lightly on the section of stem to be wounded and then twisted to remove the bark. The wound created is a little crude, but this technique will have the desired effect of stimulating root initiation, and it is much quicker.

The 'girdle' can then be dusted with auxin powder or painted with auxin gel (use a hardwood strength formulation). Then a square of black plastic or extra strong aluminium foil, large enough to allow a generous amount (a couple of handfuls) of medium to be enclosed in it, is cut and wrapped around the stem, making sure the girdle is completely covered. It is then tied securely at each end and labelled appropriately. Every few weeks it is a good idea to check the layer—it is not necessary to unwrap it, just make sure it is not drying out unduly. Once roots are emerging from the medium, the layer can be cut from the stock plant and potted up. I recommend potting the layer rather than transplanting it directly into the ground, especially if the layer is supporting a large shoot. Other specialised methods of layering can be found later in this chapter.

Aerial Layering of Eucalyptus in Brazil

Layering is a technique that is very useful for difficult to root plants and it can be used as a way of generating stock plants for subsequent production by cuttings. A good example of this is the genus *Eucalyptus*, which is normally extremely difficult to propagate from stem cuttings. Species of eucalypt that are used for forestry, such as *E. globulus* (Tasmanian blue gum) and *E. deglupta*, display great genetic variability when grown from seed. Individual trees that are far superior are propagated vegetatively in countries such as Brazil and the Philippines by first coppicing the tree (cutting it to ground level). The subsequent vigorous regrowth is aerial layered, and the resulting plants are put into rows. New shoots are then taken as cuttings. In this way, aerial layering can rejuvenate the original adult trees.

■ **Propagation environment:** One of the beauties of this method of propagation is that it can be done on the parent plant wherever it is growing. After the layer has rooted, putting the pot into a sheltered position such

Passionflowers (*Passiflora* species) can be readily propagated by serpentine layering. *Melinda Bargwanna*

as a shadehouse for a few weeks will give the most reliable result.

- **Time of year:** Layering can be commenced at any time of the year, but will be quickest if done at the beginning of the growing season (usually this means early spring). This allows the layer plenty of time to establish itself and be removed and allowed to re-establish in a pot before winter sets in. It is, however, quite possible to start a layer at any time through the warmer months of the year, but in such cases it may be advisable to leave it on the plant until winter is over.
- **Things to look for in the stock plant:** A large healthy plant that has plenty of well developed shoots. If in a home garden situation, make sure the parent plant will not be disfigured once the layer is removed. Avoid using the leading shoot (leader) as an aerial layer on species which are upright in habit.

Additional Methods of Layering

Tip Layering

This method is suitable for plants that produce flexible stems that can be easily bent down to ground level. This includes all of the climbing plants, from the wonga wonga vine (*Pandorea pandorana*) and bower of beauty (*Pandorea jasminoides*) to exotic favourites such as wisteria, philodendron and jasmine. Plants which produce multi-stemmed clumps such as various berry fruits like raspberries are also suited to this method. In early spring the shoot tips are bent down to ground level and totally covered with soil or some other suitable medium. The tip takes root and after a few weeks emerges from the medium and forms a new plant that can be removed from the parent plant at any time after it has rooted. This method has the advantage of being very quick and simple.

Serpentine (compound) layering

This is a variation on tip and simple layering that can be used on plants with very flexible stems such as climbers. As the name suggests, a snake-like layer is created by bending a single stem so that several nodes of the stem are buried with alternate nodes being exposed. The exposed nodes will produce

Plants such as ornamental ginger *(Hedychium gardnerianum)* top left are well suited to division while the Aztec lily *(Sprekelia)* top right is a wonderful candidate for separation. Bottom: Ivory Curl plant *(Buckinghamia celsissima)* can be propagated by aerial layering.

shoots so that several new plants are created from the one stem. The obvious advantage of this method is that many more plants can be propagated from each stock plant. Once again, the various wounding treatments can be applied to the buried sections of the stem.

Mound (stool) layering

Many species do not lend themselves to simple or tip layering because the shoots are stiff and upright growing and therefore cannot be easily bent down to soil level as these other methods require. Mound layering avoids this problem by taking the medium to the shoot, rather than the other way about. The crown of the plant is completely buried and the shoots take root and are subsequently removed and potted up. Although the idea of mounding the soil up over the crown contradicts all the things we are taught about growing trees and shrubs, there are a number of species that are quite happy to be buried in this fashion, including azaleas and some *Prunus* species. This method tends to be limited to commercial situations, as the treatment has a rather dramatic effect on the mother plant.

The basic idea is that an established plant is cut back to just above ground level at the beginning of the growing season (spring in most cases). When the new shoots sprout from the base of the plant, a suitably well-aerated medium (see the start of this chapter) is built up so as to cover the base of the new shoots. This has the effect of blanching them and thus stimulating root formation. This method is used quite extensively in the northern hemisphere for fruit tree production for crops such as apple rootstocks. In this context, the stock plants are planted in rows. The mounding operation takes place in spring and by the end of the growing season the medium is scraped back and the layers are cut off the stock plant and potted up or transplanted to another outdoor bed. The stock plants can be used in this way for many years, provided they are not subject to any major pest or disease problems.

Mound layering has not, to my knowledge, been applied to Australian plants at any level. It would seem, though, that there could be great potential for applying the technique to a number of difficult to strike Australian woody plants such as *Eucalyptus*, *Banksia* cultivars and *Telopea* (waratah) cultivars. Eucalypts in particular are very difficult to grow from cuttings, but it is possible to strike cuttings of many species through manipulation of stock plants, and mound layering offers a fairly straightforward method of doing just that.

Top left: Clumping plants such as *Brachycome multifida* will often self layer and then sections can be removed and potted up. Top right and bottom: Aerial layering of *Grevillea longifolia*.

Many Australian plants produce swollen underground stems called ligno-tubers that are capable of producing an almost limitless supply of new shoots, and these could perhaps be adapted to the mound layering technique.

Trench layering

Along with mound layering, this is a method that lends itself to species that are stiff and upright growing and therefore cannot be easily bent down to soil level as most other layering methods require. It is a method that demands that the stock plants be dedicated to layering. It is, therefore, a method that is probably not much applicable to the home garden. The stock plants are arranged in trenched rows and are planted at a 45 degree angle so that they can be bent right over and pegged down so that they are flat on the ground in the trench. It is a method that is normally applied to deciduous trees and shrubs and is done in late winter while the plants are still leafless. As in mound layering, the young shoots that emerge from the dormant buds are buried at their bases as they grow, and the darkened stem bases take root and are usually left until they become dormant in autumn before they are lifted and cut from the stock plant. Stock plants can be used for a number of years with this method.

Theory of Layering

There are many variations on the basic theme of layering, but all of them, of course, rely on the ability of the plant to form new roots on the stem (roots that are known as adventitious roots). Many of the principles that apply to stem cuttings also apply to layering, including the use of auxins, wounding of the stem, choosing the appropriate time of year and in particular blanching and etiolation. These subjects are all covered in detail in Chapter 4 on stem cuttings, and the methods described there apply equally to layering. Etiolation refers to the formation of new growth in darkness, while blanching is the placing of a pre-existing stem section in darkness. Both methods can be successfully applied as a pre-treatment for stem cuttings, but they are even more applicable to the various techniques of layering. Aerial, simple and serpentine (compound) layering take advantage of blanching, while mound and trench layering involve etiolation or blanching.

Another key to successful layering is wounding of the stem in the region where we want the new root system to form. Wounding refers to cutting through the bark or epidermis and exposing the vascular (conducting) tissue. This stimulates the cells there to form adventitious roots. The process of wounding can be done in a number of ways with the most simple being to make a longitudinal slice in the stem about 2 centimetres long and a third of the thickness of the stem deep. An even more effective means of wounding is the technique known as girdling, described in the methods section earlier in this chapter. This involves removing a circle of bark from the stem section where the roots will be formed, or alternatively a small length of wire is twisted tightly around the stem so that it constricts the bark. At first sight one would think that this technique is akin to ringbarking, but if done correctly, this is not the case. If girdling is done properly, only the bark and phloem tissue is removed, leaving the xylem underneath intact. This means that on the one hand, the xylem continues to allow water and mineral nutrients from the roots up to the leaves of the layer. On the other hand, because the phloem is completely interrupted, all the sugars and naturally occurring auxins and growth factors produced in the shoot tip and leaves of the layer collect at the top of the girdle cut, precisely where the root system forms. This technique only applies to dicotyledons which have their xylem and phloem in a ring around the outside of the stem. Monocotyledons such as cordylines, in contrast, have their vascular tissue in bundles scattered throughout the stem. In these cases the slice method should be used.

An essential part of most layering techniques is the wounding of the stem. This interrupts the flow of sap from the leaves to the roots and results in carbohydrates and natural auxins from the shoots collecting at the top of the wounded area. This area will often become distinctly swollen before the new roots emerge. The natural auxins produced in the shoot tip will obviously help to stimulate root formation and lessens the need for artificial auxins to be applied.

The time of year can also be a critical factor in achieving high success rates. Generally speaking, the best time for most plants is around the time they start their new growth for the year—in other words, late winter or early spring. In warmer climates where temperatures encourage growth over a longer period there is a lot more flexibility, and it is feasible to start layers throughout the warmer months. Remember the longer the growing season, the bigger the plants will be able to grow, so from this point of view it is probably ideal to start the layers as early as possible.

Layering can be a particularly useful technique where small numbers of lots of different cultivars of a particular plant are required, such as at a specialist camellia or hibiscus nursery. Often such nurseries have extensive display gardens devoted to their cultivar collections. Aerial layering can be used to selectively multiply cultivars so that small numbers of relatively large plants are produced.

In summary, layering represents a great alternative when there are limited options for controlling the propagation environment. A method can be found for many types of plant, and with a little bit of creative thinking techniques can be modified to hasten the process if large numbers of plants are required.

CHAPTER 8

Division
and
Separation

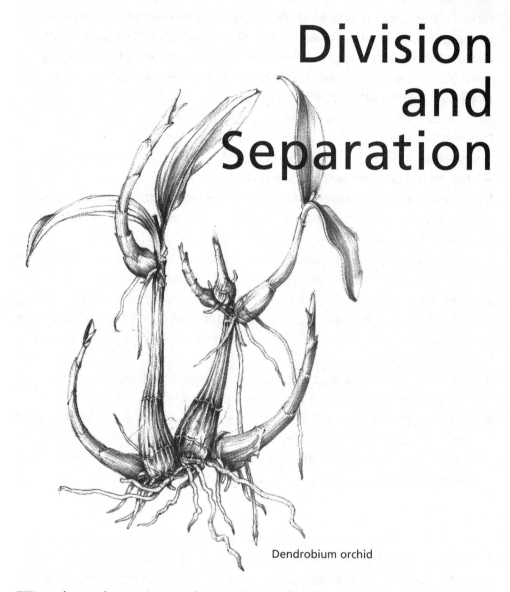

Dendrobium orchid

Perhaps the easiest and most basic of all propagation methods is to take a clumping style of plant and break it up into smaller sections that will go on to become self-sustaining plants. Plants such as kangaroo paws, agapanthus and mondo grass are admirably suited to this method of propagation.

There is a whole category of plants called **geophytes** that, as the name suggests, have most of their action happening at or below ground level. To understand how a geophyte has evolved, think of a normal woody plant stem as a collapsible telescope that is fully extended. Now imagine compressing it to its smallest dimensions—you now have a typical geophyte, in which all the buds are pressed down into a flat base (in bulbs, known as the basal plate). This compressed shoot stays at ground level until it is triggered to flower, and then it rapidly elongates giving us the characteristic flower stems found on this group of plants. Such structures include:

- rhizomes (creeping underground stems).
- stolons (creeping above ground stems).
- stem tubers—the swollen end of an underground stem, such as those in potatoes, that bears buds (or 'eyes') in axils of scale-like rudimentary leaves. Its function is to store water and nutrients.
- root tubers—a swollen root that bears buds at the top, such as found in dahlias. Its function is to store water and nutrients.
- pseudobulbs—a swollen stem base, usually found in orchids such as cymbidiums. Its function is to store water and nutrients, and it differs from a true bulb in that it has dormant buds on the outside of the structure.
- bulbs—a modified shoot that is highly compressed and is enclosed by fleshy, scale-like leaves, as in onions and tulips.
- corms—a modified, swollen stem base bearing buds on the outside of the stem in the axils of scale-like remains of leaves from the previous season's growth. Unlike the pseudobulb, a new corm is produced each season on top of the previous season's corm.

A distinction can be made between **separation**, which applies to plant types such as bulbs and corms in which independent structures called bulblets and cormlets are formed and naturally split from the parent plant, and **division**, which applies to all the other geophyte structures in which the new plantlets must be physically cut or broken from the parent plant.

Most geophyte structures have evolved in response to regular annual environmental stress such as summer drought or freezing conditions in winter. A bulb, corm or rhizome gives the plant the capacity to die back to ground level and remain dormant until suitable growing conditions return. Once we understand their annual cycle of dormancy and growth, we will be in a much better position to propagate them successfully.

Saving for a Rainy Day   The rain lilies (*Zephyranthes*) are a typical example of the way in which the specialised structure of geophytes, in this case bulbs, has evolved to help the plant cope with environmental stress. The rain lilies are native to warm climates in Texas, Mexico and the West Indies, where rain falls somewhat unpredictably throughout the year. Most species have the capacity in the wild to spring up and flower opportunistically at any time during spring and summer when moisture arrives. Of course, in a garden situation we can regulate flowering by irrigating the plants.

Division

- **Medium:** Divided clumps are usually not very fussy with regard to media, and it is often quite possible to put them straight into open ground. Any reasonable general purpose potting mix will be quite suitable for potting up divisions.
- **Container:** If divisions are potted, match the container reasonably closely to the volume of the potential new root ball of the clump you are potting (remembering that a lot of the roots have often been damaged or removed during the division process). In other words, don't try to jam a large piece into a small pot because when the roots re-establish they will not have sufficient medium for optimum growth. On the other hand, avoid using a pot that is much bigger than the estimated root ball after re-establishment. The problem in this case is that a small clump in a large volume of potting mix may stay too moist and possibly rot out.
- **Method:** Most species can be handled quite roughly when it comes to division. A garden fork is the ideal tool for lifting most plants, as it preserves as much of the old root system as possible. Be warned, however, as some species

will need considerably more than a garden fork to budge them. Once the clump is lifted it may be split, either by hand or, for tougher customers, with an old bread knife, a spade or even an axe. Look for natural planes of division through the clump when cutting, so that you do not slice through too many intact shoots. For maximum success, the division should normally contain at least three to four shoots, although it is certainly possible to divide off single shoots if you are prepared to put more effort into their care in the succeeding weeks. If the division will receive minimal attention, such as going straight into an open ground situation, keep them on the larger side. Cut away any dead or diseased parts of the clump, whether they be leaves, stem or roots. It is also a good idea to remove the top centimetre of the original soil from the division, as this top soil often harbours large quantities of weed seed. For most species it is a good practice to reduce the foliage by about half as this will put less demand on the root system while it is repairing itself. For species which are known to rot easily, it may be worth dusting the cut stem surfaces with a fungicide such as sulphur as a preventative measure. Then simply plant the division, ensuring the medium comes up to the same level as in the undivided plant.

Bird Battles   The bird of paradise (*Strelitzia reginae*) is perfectly suited to division and it is not uncommon for clumps of it to reach several metres in diameter. A word of warning, however. Its tough roots and stems give it an iron grip on the soil, and it will require an extraordinary effort to dislodge it by hand. A mechanical digger such as a backhoe will save many hours of back-breaking work, as well as doing less damage to the plant.

- **Propagation environment:** It is preferable for the divided plant to go into a sheltered environment such as a shadehouse until new roots can be observed growing out of the bottom of the pot.
- **Time of year:** The perfect time is just at the end of the dormant season (which will be the end of winter for many species). It is generally possible to divide at other times of the year, but this may involve sacrificing a crop of flowers which may be forming at the time. Most species become active in winter or spring, and their flowers develop during the growing

season and are borne in spring or summer. If division is done during this flower development phase, these flowers will often abort as the plant cannot supply enough water to them.

- **Things to look for in the stock plant:** The plant should be free of pests and diseases, as the tool used for dividing will spread any disease-causing organism through your whole stock. In addition, it is useful to divide clumps which have become large and overgrown and consequently have declined in vigour and flowering performance.

Dahlia Dalliance In ancient Mexico the Aztecs cultivated dahlias not only for their classical daisy flowers, but also for their edible fleshy, swollen roots. The climate in the highland areas to which they are native is very dry in the cooler months of the year and it is at this time that dahlias are dormant. When rains start at the beginning of spring, the plants sprout and grow rapidly, flowering through summer and autumn. After flowering the plants gradually die back to ground level and enter their dormant period. Dahlias grown in areas with wet winters will require special attention, as the root tubers may rot out if left in the ground during dormancy. In this case, it is best to lift them as soon as they become dormant in autumn and store them in a dry, well-aerated situation until spring. Areas with dry winters are perfect for growing dahlias, as they can be left to their own devices and do not need to be lifted every year. Only when the clumps become overgrown and the flowering performance declines does one need to lift the clumps with a garden fork and divide them. In the case of dahlias, each division must have at least one swollen fleshy root as each of these contains several buds or eyes which enable the plant to regenerate.

Separation

- **Medium:** The medium is not crucial for this method of propagation
- **Container:** Most containers are suitable for repotting separated bulbs and corms
- **Method:** There is very little skill to master with this propagation method as bulbs and corms have this wonderful characteristic of wanting to split apart spontaneously. For most species it is like digging potatoes—a

garden fork or spade is used to lift the clump. A sieve with a fairly coarse mesh is a very handy tool if you are doing large quantities. A piece of fly screen can be easily adapted to make a sieve. Bulbs and corms can also be graded at this stage into two or three sizes, with the largest ones being guaranteed to flower and the smaller ones generally needing a year or two to increase in size before they flower.

Gladiolus Be careful when you are lifting a species that you are not familiar with, as you may be surprised at how small the bulblets and cormlets at the base of the main bulb or corm can be. An example is gladiolus which for most garden varieties has a very large corm, in some varieties being as big as a small fist. However, there may be up to a hundred cormlets at the base, with some being no bigger than a pin-head. In this situation it is virtually inevitable that you will miss some cormlets, but if you are really keen to save every last one, the screened soil can be put into a pot and watered and any stray cormlets should grow out into larger structures which will be readily spotted.

■ **Propagation environment:** There are no specific requirements, as most bulbs and corms are planted outdoors. They can also be grown in intensive cultivation in controlled environments.

■ **Time of year:** Separation should be carried out at the end of the growing season for the particular species in question. Most bulbs and corms have a distinct dormant season when the foliage dies down completely and the best time to lift and separate them is obvious. After flowering there is usually a period of a number of weeks during which the foliage stays green, and a dose of fertiliser then will help to build up the bulb or corm for the following season. It is also important to recognise that in many species the flower bud for the following season is formed during this period, so do not be too hasty about lifting your bulbs and corms.

■ **Things to look for in the stock plant:** A clump of bulbs or corms should be free of any major pest and disease infestations. In addition, it is a good idea to wait until a clump becomes overcrowded before undertaking separation. Commercial production of bulbs and corms often involves a preventative hot water soaking treatment—the bulbs or corms are held at around 45 degrees Celsius for four hours. This is sufficient to control most pests and diseases.

Evergreen Bulbs

Some bulb-forming species are capable of altering their growth habit when given better growing conditions. Plants such as hippeastrums can form evergreen clumps that never die down when grown in frost-free conditions with year-round moisture. In such cases we propagate them by dividing the plants up when they have finished their flowering period. It is also a good idea to remove about half of the leaves by cutting them back with a sharp knife.

Bulb Types

There are two distinct types of bulb structures and it is very important for plant propagators to understand the distinction between them. The first and most common type is the **tunicate bulb,** which has a dry, membranous brown 'skin' enclosing the succulent, fleshy scale leaves within. This 'tunic' has an obvious function of protecting the bulb from drying out. Typical examples include onions, daffodils and tulips. The second and far less common type is the **non-tunicate bulb,** which has fleshy, succulent small scales that overlap right to the outside of the bulb. The classic example of this type is the true lilies (*Lilium* species). An important practical difference between the two types is that non-tunicate bulbs must not be allowed to dry out during storage. This is avoided by storing the bulbs in slightly moist peat moss or an equivalent such as coconut fibre. Another point with non-tunicate bulbs is that the fleshy scales can be detached and used for propagation purposes. The small triangular-shaped scales can either be planted in a well drained medium with the base buried slightly, or a number of scales can be mixed into a bag of vermiculite and stored under cool and slightly moist conditions. After a few months tiny little bulblets form on the base of the scales.

Bulb Cuttage and Twin Scaling

For those who are too impatient to wait for their bulbs to multiply naturally and then separate them as outlined above, there is an ingenious technique known as bulb cuttage which can be used to speed things up a bit. It basically involves cutting the bulb into a number of sections so that each bit contains a part of the bulb's compressed stem (known as the basal plate). The basal plate not only houses the apical meristem (the growing tip), but also many axillary buds which can be induced to grow and form themselves into new bulbs.

- **Medium:** Because it exposes a great deal of soft damaged tissue this method requires a very clean medium, such as pure vermiculite, or a more standard medium that has been pasteurised.
- **Container:** Any sort of container can be used. If large quantities are being grown, the bulb pieces can be put into a plastic bag and mixed with vermiculite, placed in a warm place for several weeks, and then potted up.
- **Method:** Most of us are familiar with the process of cutting up an onion, a typical bulb. The onion rings produced are actually cross sections of the leaves (which in their modified form in bulbs are known as leaf scales). The basal plate, that tough bit of tissue at the base of the onion actually contains all the vegetative buds. For bulb cuttage we slice bulbs longitudinally (in the opposite direction to that in which an onion is usually cut), so that each cut goes through the top and bottom of the bulb. Most bulbs can be cut into eight sections, with each section having a part of the basal plate attached. Very large bulbs, such as hippeastrums or belladonna lilies (*Amaryllis belladonna*), can be cut into 16 equal pieces. Each of these pieces will look a little like a 'potato wedge' with a little bit of solid tissue of the basal plate at its base. These pieces can then be planted into a pot with the bottom part (including the basal plate) being buried in the medium. It should form a small bulb or bulbs by the end of the growing season and these can then be handled like normal bulbs. Other methods, known as scooping, scoring and coring can also be used. These are detailed in the theory section of this chapter.
- **Time of year:** The technique is best carried out in autumn for species that are just about to come out of dormancy, such as daffodils and tulips. For species such as belladonna lilies and nerines that have their

growing season through spring and summer rather than winter, it is best to carry out twin scaling in spring.

- **Things to look for in the stock plant:** It is absolutely critical that the bulbs used are free of pests and diseases as any that are present will be rapidly spread through the whole stock.

Theory of Division and Separation

The actual process of separation is a very simple one, since the bulbs and corms literally fall apart when removed from the soil or potting mix they have been grown in. One of the most important considerations is timing the operation so that the plant is at the optimum stage for separation. As this is when the plants are dormant, the actual time will vary from species to species. For spring flowering bulbs and corms, late summer to early autumn, after the foliage dies down, is the time to lift and separate. Other bulbs, such as the naked ladies (*Amaryllis belladonna*) and golden spider lilies (*Lycoris aurea*), flower in the autumn, make vegetative growth through winter and become dormant in spring, at which time they can be lifted and separated. Therefore it is extremely important to study the species you are working with to discover the optimum time for separation.

There are also several other specialised methods of vegetative propagation of bulbs. Hyacinths and lachenalias readily form adventitious shoots on the bases of their leaves. Several methods which encourage this have been developed over the years. These all have in common the fact that the apical meristem (growing tip) of the bulb is destroyed and the bases of the leaf scales are exposed and wounded. **Scooping** refers to using a teaspoon or a specially curved knife to remove the basal plate from the bottom of the bulb. The bulb is then left upturned for a week or so to callus over, and then planted as normal. With hyacinths, anything up to 50 tiny bulblets will then form on the base of the bulb and these can be removed at the end of the growing season and handled as any normal bulb would be. **Scoring** refers to using a normal knife to make two vertical cuts in the base of the bulb, thus forming a cross shape. The cuts must be deep enough to go right through the basal plate and destroy the apical meristem. The bulbs are then handled as described above for scooped bulbs. **Coring** refers to using a cylindrical tool such as an apple corer to remove a cylinder of tissue from the basal plate. The bulbs are then handled as descibed above for scooped bulbs. For all three techniques, numerous bulblets form along the cut surfaces and after growing on for one season they can be separated from the parent bulb. Like twin scaling, these methods greatly speed up the multiplication rate for impatient propagators.

Both division and separation processes rely on the removal of side (axillary) shoots from a main shoot (or a clump of main shoots). With most species, multiplication rates are fairly high and there are plenty of shoots to work with. There are, however, species which do not multiply quickly (e.g. *Clivia*), or situations in which we have a limited number of stock plants and wish to increase them rapidly. In such cases, destruction of the apical meristem can be used to break down apical dominance and stimulate the growth of dormant axillary (side) buds. The technique involves a tool such as a knitting needle being used to poke into the top of the shoot and macerate the shoot tip (apical meristem). This should be done at the beginning of the growing season (spring for most species), but please note, this is highly likely to abort the flower stem from that particular shoot, although this also has the bonus of the plant channelling more energy into vegetative growth.

The critical factor in division and separation is studying the species you are working with to ensure that you have the timing right. Most plants that are suited to this method of propagation have a distinct dormant period, and it is during this period that the plant can be very vulnerable to pests and diseases, particularly if the climate in the dormant period is wetter than the plant normally experiences in the wild. In this circumstance, it may be necessary to lift and store the plant during the dormant period in order to ensure its survival.

Hippeastrum hybrids are easily propagated by separation. *Fred Meyer*

CHAPTER 9

Budding and Grafting

G rafting and budding are usually discussed under the same heading as they are essentially the same technique. Both involve taking a bud or stem section from one plant and attaching it to a different plant in such a way that the two meld together to form a single plant that combines desirable characteristics of both. It is very much a case of 'the whole being much greater than the sum of the parts'.

The inspiration for grafting probably first arose from the observation of natural grafting in wild forests. A wide variety of species such as Sydney red gum (*Angophora costata*), common ivy (*Hedera helix*), ash (*Fraxinus excelsior*) and poplars (*Populus* species) all commonly form unions in their own branches by natural grafting. In formal gardens of the nineteenth century natural grafting was often seen where trees were twisted and tied together in imitations of columns and balustrades.

A few definitions are necessary before we go any further. The **scion** forms the top of the grafted plant, while the **rootstock** forms the root system. The term **budding** is used when the scion consists of a single bud on a small piece of bark, while **grafting** is normally used to refer to a scion that is a stem section with multiple buds. The key to success lies in the **graft union**, the area of contact between the scion and the rootstock. The essential point is that there needs to be a blending between the cambial tissues of the two

Because of their large bulb size new cultivars such as this Fred Meyer-bred Hippeastrum, *Fred Myer*, (top right) can be rapidly multiplied by bulb cuttage (twin scaling). Gladiolus, *Fred Myer*, (top left) are easily propagated by separation of the numerous cormlets on the base of the mother corms. Peruvian lilies (*Alstroemeria* species), *Fred Myer*, (bottom left) and the native iris (*Patersonia glabrata*), *Melinda Bargwanna*, are both multiplied by division.

plants, i.e. that area of tissue just beneath the bark that is growing and giving rise to new xylem and phloem. If the two plants are genetically compatible, a strong union will form that will be capable of supporting a mature tree or shrub. Further detail on this process is given later in this chapter.

Grafting

- **Medium:** Grafting can be done on a rootstock which is growing in the ground or in a pot, and thus the medium is not critical, provided it is adequate for the growth of the rootstock. Since most rootstocks are specifically chosen for their hardiness and adaptability, there is a wide range of suitable media.
- **Container:** If the rootstock is not grown in soil, a container that comfortably holds it is ideal. Once the graft has taken, the plant will be potted on as it grows bigger, and the roots start to protrude from the drainage holes of the pot.
- **Method:** A whole book could be, and indeed has been, written on the subject of grafting (see Further Reading *The Grafter's Handbook* by R.J. Garner, 1957). There are numerous variations of technique to suit differ-

Approach graft of *Grevillea* 'Poorinda Royal Mantle' onto *Grevillea robusta*. The scion is taped onto the stem with the base in a vial of water to help it through till the graft union forms.

ent species and situations, and these are covered fully in the theory section of this chapter. As an introduction to grafting, a handy method is the approach graft, where the scion is actually part of a potted plant that is placed next to the rootstock. In this method, the scion is nursed along by its own root system while the graft union is forming. It is a wonderful way of creating a weeping standard grafted plant. A thin slice of bark 2–5 centimetres long and 1–2 centimetres wide is removed from both the scion and rootsock to expose the vascular cambium. The cut surfaces are then united so that the vascular cambium of the rootstock is matched with that of the scion over as wide a surface area as possible. The united sections are then tied together with grafting tape over their whole length so as to exclude as much water as possible. When a graft is first carried out, it is important to reduce the amount of foliage on the scion. If no protection can be afforded, it may be desirable to remove all the foliage from the scion. It is important to use a specialised grafting or budding knife, which can be obtained from specialist horticultural supply houses.

- **Propagation environment:** Where the newly grafted plant is a potted specimen it is highly desirable that a protected environment such as a shadehouse or greenhouse be used to prevent any extreme conditions, particularly during the first few weeks after the graft has been performed.
- **Time of year:** Grafting is generally done in late winter as the rootstock and scion are coming into a growth period. It is at this time that callus growth, which enables rapid healing of the graft union, is likely to be at its best.
- **Things to look for in the stock plant:** Making sure of the identity of both scion and rootstock is critical, given the long life span of the plant. Freedom from diseases, particularly viruses, is also of paramount importance and with some crops it is possible to obtain virus-indexed material (see theory section for further details).

Cutting Grafts

This rather intriguing method involves preparing the rootstock as a cutting and grafting the scion onto it, all in a single operation. It is a rather high-risk option as it is a lot to ask of the plants, but it does work reasonably well where you are using a rootstock which is relatively easily rooted, such as *Camellia sasanqua* with other camellia species as scions.

- **Medium:** It is vital that a porous, well-aerated mix is provided to ensure the cutting that forms the rootstock strikes as quickly as possible. A mix of 50% per litre of coarse sand and 50% peat or coconut fibre will be quite adequate.
- **Container:** The cutting grafts are best planted into individual tubes. Deep containers such as forestry (tree) tubes are ideal.
- **Method:** If we take camellias as an example, a standard semi-hardwood cutting of *Camellia sasanqua* is prepared and a scion of a hard to propagate camellia such as some *C. reticulata* cultivars is either top cleft or whip and tongue grafted onto it (see details of these techniques later in this chapter). Most of the foliage is removed from the scion (leaving say two leaves only) to reduce the stress on the graft. It is important to use a specialised grafting or budding knife, which can be obtained from specialist horticultural supply houses.
- **Propagation environment:** A normal humidity-controlled environment as would be used for a semi-hardwood cutting should be provided. Humidity will be gradually reduced as growth of the scion commences.
- **Time of year:** Autumn is the ideal time for the camellia example. For other plants the ideal time may be different depending on the species.
- **Things to look for in the stock plant:** High health and correct identity.

Budding

- **Medium:** The rootstocks used for budding may be either plants in pots, or established plants growing in soil._
- **Container:** There are no particular requirements for containers for budded plants.
- **Method:** There are a number of different techniques used but we will focus on the most common one here, namely 'T' budding (also known as shield budding). This involves making a T-shaped cut that goes just through the bark a few cm above the base of the rootstock, and enables the bark to be peeled back. The area of the rootstock where the T cut is made should be free of buds. A single bud is then cut from the scion plant so that the bud is on a small shield shaped piece of bark. This shield is then slipped under the peeled back bark of the T cut on the rootstock. The bud is then fixed in place by pushing the flaps of the T cut back in place, and the whole thing wrapped up in budding tape. When the bud starts to sprout, the tape is removed. Once the bud has grown out to a

few centimetres, the shoot of the rootstock above the scion can be trimmed off, leaving only the scion shoot. It is important to use a specialised grafting or budding knife, which can be obtained from specialist horticultural supply houses.

- **Propagation environment:** Budding is usually done outdoors quite successfully. However, if budding is done in pots, it is a good idea to grow them in a protected environment such as a shadehouse or greenhouse.
- **Time of year:** Budding must be done when the rootstock is in active growth when the sap is flowing and the bark can be easily peeled back to enable the bud to be inserted. During this time the bark is said to be **'lifting'** or **'slipping'**. This can occur right through the warmer months, from spring to summer.
- **Things to look for in the stock plant:** Making sure of the identity of both scion and rootstock is critical, given the long life span of the plant. Freedom from diseases, particularly viruses, is also of paramount importance and with many crops it is possible to obtain virus-indexed material (see theory section for further details).

Theory of Budding and Grafting

There are a number of reasons for budding and grafting, including:

1. Creating a plant with an improved root system. Many rootstocks are selected for their tolerance to poor conditions and/or root diseases. This a matter of determining what will be the major stresses in your particular situation. Root diseases caused by fungi such as *Phytophthora* or acid soil conditions are examples of the types of problems that can be overcome through the use of rootstocks. A good example is the use in the propagation of roses of rootstocks such as *Rosa multiflora*, which provides adaptability to a wide range of soil types.

2. Perpetuating an outstanding seedling as a cultivar. A significant number of woody plants, particularly trees, are difficult to propagate by cuttings or other methods and so grafting or budding becomes the next most feasible method of vegetative propagation. For instance, the Illawarra flame tree (*Brachychiton acerifolium*) at its best is one of the world's most spectacular flowering trees, with the whole tree being alight with

red flowers. Many specimens of this species fail to flower as well as one would like, and often the reason is that they were propagated from seed which was not genetically predisposed to flower profusely. To remedy this, scion wood can be taken from specimens that do consistently flower well and grafted onto seedling material. In general, in this type of situation the rootstock is usually of the same species as the scion.

Mighty Mint Bushes

An extensive amount of research has been carried out at the Australian National Botanic Gardens on using coastal rosemary (*Westringia fruticosa*) as a rootstock for the native mint bushes (*Prostanthera* species). Coastal rosemary is renowned as one of the hardiest of all Australian plants in cultivation, while the native mint bushes are notoriously short-lived, often dying suddenly due to root rotting fungi such as *Phytopthora*. The grafted specimens extend the life of the mint bush from a few years to up to 20 or so. The extra expense of grafting is justified in creating a much longer lived plant.

Left: Grevillea nudiflora makes a superb weeping standard when grafted onto silky oak (*G. robusta*). Right: Top-working of avocados — a small scion is grafted onto a 40-year-old tree that has been lopped.

3. Creating 'novelty' plants. Both grafting and budding can be used to create novel plant forms and types such as **weeping standards** (a single stemmed rootstock grown to a height of a couple of metres, with a prostrate scion grafted on top, creating an umbrella-like shape when the scion grows out). 'Fruit salad plants' are another popular novelty type with several fruit tree varieties grafted or budded onto the same tree—for instance, you can have a citrus tree that has lemon, orange and mandarin scions. Such a tree will usually require some maintenance pruning to keep the different scions in balance as the most vigorous one will tend to take over if not pruned back selectively.

Grieving Grevilleas

The silky oak (*Grevillea robusta*) is one of the few of the 250-odd species of grevillea that grows into a tree. It has been extensively used as a rootstock for other grevillea species, particularly those with a prostrate growth habit, i.e. ground covering plants. The best known is the cultivar 'Poorinda Royal Mantle', which, when grafted onto a 2–3 metre high silky oak creates a wonderful cascading plant that flowers for most of the year. **Top cleft or wedge grafting** is the technique normally used in creating weeping standards (see details later in this chapter).

4. Repairing damaged trees. A couple of grafting methods have been developed for trees which need urgent 'surgery' to ensure their survival. Where a tree has been ringbarked the reason why death occurs is that the vascular system which transports water and nutrients is completely removed. A **bridge graft** (see details below) is used to 'transplant' a new vascular system onto the tree by taking a small shoot from another part of the same tree (or another tree of the same species) and grafting it onto the tree such that it 'bridges' the gap across the ringbarked section. Another fascinating technique is known as **inarching**, a technique that is used to repair trees or shrubs whose root system is dying. The plant to be used as the rootstock is planted at the foot of the dying plant and the two are then grafted at the foot of the trunk. Obviously one would to and select a very hardy rootstock as root disease is usually the reason that such a graft is needed, although disturbance to the root system or changes to drainage patterns through earthworks are other possible causes.

5. Changing the cultivar of an existing tree or shrub. Sometimes situations occur where the established planting is no longer wanted and rather than remove the plant(s), grafting or budding can be used to quickly establish a different cultivar. This process is known as **top-working** or **top-grafting**, and is the method often used in fruit orchards when changing tastes have decreed that certain varieties are no longer marketable.

Formation of the graft union

An essential condition for the formation of a successful graft union is having the cambial tissues of rootstock and scion in close contact in conditions favourable to growth. The **vascular cambium** is a thin layer of cells situated just beneath the bark of a woody plant. It is meristematic tissue which means it is made up of actively growing cells which give rise to the vascular (conducting) tissue of the plant—xylem, which transports water from the roots to the leaves, and phloem, which conducts sugars from the leaves to all other parts of the plant.

The vascular cambium is not difficult to find on an actively growing woody plant. Take a stem section of such a plant and use a knife to cut into the bark until you feel a little 'clunk', signalling that you have gone through the bark and hit woody tissue. Now slip your thumbnail into the cut and peel away the bark. In an actively growing plant there will be a slippery, distinctly moist layer that is the vascular cambium. It is this layer of tissue in the rootstock and the scion that must be joined. The trap for young players is that the bark may be of different thicknesses in rootstock and scion, and if the outer layers of bark are set so they are flush this will mean that the cambium layers will fail to match and the graft will be unsuccessful. This situation commonly arises when the rootsock and scion are of different ages, with the older stem usually having much thicker bark than the younger stem (usually the scion).

The key to successful grafting and budding is to achieve the maximum possible contact between the rootstock and scion, and to secure the union for the weeks or months it takes for the cells to grow together to form a union strong enough to support the scion independently. The graft union is normally secured by tying it with special **grafting tape**. In addition, methods such as the whip and tongue graft (see details later in this chapter) have been developed which give a splint-like structure that holds the scion in place while a union is forming.

Further Notes on Grafting and Budding Techniques

There is a number of different methods of grafting and budding and the choice will depend on the type of plant material and climatic conditions available.

Budding

Budding is sometimes referred to as bud grafting since it relies on exactly the same principles as grafting, namely the formation of a union between the cambium tissue of rootstock and scion. Budding, however, has a couple of significant advantages over grafting that have led to it becoming an extremely widely-practised technique. Since only a single bud is required in budding, as opposed to several for grafting, much more efficient use is made of scionwood, which is often expensive and/or limited in quantity. The union formed by budding is usually much stronger than that of a graft, sometimes leading to a much longer-lived plant. Budding is generally a much simpler process, which means that it is a technique more easily mastered by amateurs.

Right: A massive graft union on a decades-old elm tree.

Budding can be done during the warmer months of the year, from spring right through to autumn, provided that the rootstock is in active growth, which in turn means that the bark will be 'slipping' and therefore able to be easily lifted to enable insertion of the bud. In commercial situations budding tends to be done in autumn, as this allows time for rootstocks to be propagated in spring and then grown on so that by autumn the base of the rootstock has reached 1–2 centimetres in diameter, making it a comfortable size to work with. If the rootstock is more than a season old, it will normally be big enough to bud in spring, allowing for a full season's growth.

'T' or shield budding is perhaps the simplest and easiest of budding or grafting techniques, and it is the method that is used most commonly by commercial practitioners. In Australia the vast majority of citrus and rose plants are propagated using this method. The technique is outlined earlier in this chapter. There are numerous alternative budding techniques, such as **chip, patch, flute, ring and I-budding**. These are rather specialised techniques which are not commonly practised in Australia. Further details can be found in Hartmann and Kester, *Plant Propagation: Principles and Practices (see Further Reading).*

Alternative methods of grafting

It is vital for all methods of grafting that a well-sharpened grafting knife is used. Unlike most knives, the grafting knife is only bevelled on one side and completely flat on the other side. This ensures that a smooth, flat surface is created when the knife is used to cut woody stems.

- **Whip (or tongue) graft:** Whip grafts are excellent when the rootstock and scion are of similar diameters. The whip graft is performed by making a long, gently sloping cut in both the rootstock and the scion. The vascular cambiums of both are then matched as closely as possible, and then the whole graft is tied together. If the rootstock is much bigger than the scion, the vascular cambium can only be matched on one side, but this is still sufficient to give a successful result in most cases. In order to create a more stable graft, interlocking 'tongues' can be created by making cuts in the rootstock and scion about a third of the distance from the top. These cuts should be about one centimetre long. When the scion is inserted into the rootstock, the tongues interlock and hold the graft together, making it much easier to tie.
- **Top cleft (or wedge) graft:** This graft is particularly well-suited to

attaching a small scion onto a rootstock of much larger diameter. It is commonly used for top-working (changing the cultivar see photo page 116.) of long established trees and for creating weeping standards. Ideally the graft should be done in late winter, just as growth is about to recommence in rootstock and scion. Two long sloping cuts are made in the scion so that it has a tapering point. These cuts need to be smooth and are best done with a single stroke of the knife so that they are flat, ensuring maximum cambial contact on insertion. The knife is then used to make a cut down the the middle of the rootstock such that the scion can be wedged into it to ensure even contact of the cambial layers of scion and rootstock.

- **Bridge graft:** This is a very specialised graft for repairing ringbarked trees. Various problems such as rats, collar rots or 'whipper-snipper' damage to the base of the trunk can result in the bark and underlying vascular tissue being destroyed, effectively isolating the healthy roots from the crown of the tree and eventually resulting in the death of the tree. Some species are capable of producing callus tissue, which will heal the wound naturally, and this can be encouraged by covering the damaged area with moist hessian. The safest approach, however, is to carry out a bridge graft. Scion wood is best taken from the crown of the damaged tree if it is still in good condition, or from a tree of the same cultivar or species if that is the next best alternative. Small shoots 0.5–1 centimetre in diameter are taken and the leaves removed, should any be present. The damaged tree is prepared by trimming the damaged bark back to healthy tissue. As many scion shoots as possible are then inserted (in their normal orientation) to bridge the gap between the two ends of healthy bark. It is a good idea to wrap the graft in a material such as grafting tape or Parafilm® to prevent drying out of the whole area. **Inarching** and **bracing** are other types of repair graft which can be found in *The Grafter's Handbook* by R.J. Garner (see Further Reading).

Many variations in grafting technique are possible to suit different species and situations. These techniques include side veneer (spliced side), side tongue, notch or wedge (saw-kerf), bark, spliced approach, tongued approach, inlay approach, nurse-root, cotyledon (micro-graft), crown, double-working and nurse-seed grafting. Details of all these techniques can be found in Hartmann and Kester, *Plant Propagation: Principles and Practices* (see Further Reading).

Tools and accessories

Specialised budding and grafting knives are available from horticultural supply houses. A general purpose budding knife is a good starting point for the beginner as it will be quite adequate for grafting as well as budding. Grafting machines, which remove the need for skilled manual labourers, are available for large-scale production. A good sharp pair of secateurs is also essential for trimming work. A variety of methods is used to hold the scion in place, varying from plastic grafting tape to a stretchy laboratory tape such as Parafilm®. Paraffin wax or bituminous grafting emulsions or even petroleum jelly is used sometimes to seal the graft union, although this practice is by no means essential to success. Special plastic or metal clips are also available for holding the scion in place, but some searching may be required to find a suitable supplier.

Rootstocks

The choice of rootstock is vitally important as considerable improvement in the performance of the plant will result from the correct decision. Rootstocks may be propagated from seed, and as it is the cheapest method, it is usually preferred. Citrus, for instance, are almost exclusively grafted onto seed-propagated rootstocks of tri (*Poncirus trifoliata*) or rough lemon. The disadvantage of seedling rootstocks is that they are generally not genetically uniform, and therefore one can expect some variation in the performance of the finished product.

Many rootstocks are produced vegetatively by a variety of techniques. Cuttings (hardwood, semi-hardwood, softwood and root), layering and tissue culture are all used where appropriate. Vegetative propagation is used where genetically superior rootstocks have been selected through trial and error. In such cases the rootstock usually has some outstanding feature such as very good resistance to root rot. Such rootstocks are generally available from specialist propagators.

Scionwood

There are a number of important considerations when collecting material for grafting and budding. **Trueness to type** is perhaps the paramount point since the finished product will often live for many decades. Careful labelling of parent plants and scionwood is an important starting point. In many species mutations ('sporting') is not infrequent, so it is vital to observe the parent trees when they are flowering and fruiting to ensure they have remained true to type. For many fruit crops, government or industry sponsored organisations such as the Australian Citrus Propagation Association Incorporated maintain orchards specifically for the purpose of supplying 'certified' scionwood that is true to type and tested to ensure it is free of disease-causing organisms such as viruses.

Using virus-free material is also critical. Virus diseases do not often kill the plant, but they can cause severe stunting and render the plant uncommercial. The reason that virus diseases are feared above fungal and bacterial diseases is that there is no way to cure them once they are established (aside from killing the plant). Viruses are spread by sap sucking insects such as aphids and thrips, and are also spread in sap carried on tools such as knives and secateurs. It is important therefore to regularly surface sterilise tools used in grafting and budding with a sterilant such as a quaternary ammonium compound (e.g. Biogram®).

When storing scionwood, ensure that the material is not allowed to suffer any water or temperature stress whatsoever as these factors can be a major cause of failure. If the scionwood is leafy, it is best to collect it fresh and reduce the amount of foliage present by cutting leaves in half or removing half to three-quarters of them. Deciduous material should be wrapped in moist newspaper and put into a refrigerator in a plastic bag.

Compatibilitiy of rootstock and scion

The rootstock and scion plants must be genetically compatible for a successful graft union to form. This can be a rather tricky thing to predict, and some unlikely combinations can sometimes be achieved. Generally speaking, the closer the genetic relationship, the greater the likelihood of success. In terms of these relationships there are several possibilities. The simplest case is an **intraspecific graft** where two individuals of the same species are joined with a very high likelihood of success, e.g. variegated forms of the brush box tree (*Lophostemon confertus*) are grafted onto normal green seedlings of the same species. An **interspecific graft** is between plants belonging to two different species but with both being members of the same genus, e.g. some of the hardy eastern states banksias such as *B. integrifolia* can be used as rootstocks for the root rot-prone species of banksias from Western Australia such as *B. menziesii* and *B. speciosa*. While a great number of interspecific combinations are successful, there are many cases where they are not. The final combination is the **intergeneric graft** between two individuals belonging to different genera within the same family, e.g. oval-leafed mint bush (*Prostanthera ovalifolia*) grafted onto coastal rosemary (*Westringia fruticosa*). The pear (*Pyrus communis*) can be successfully grafted onto the hawthorn (*Crataegus oxycantha*).

Incompatibilty between rootstock and scion is a rather complicated issue as it may be many years before it rears its ugly head. It may occur straightaway after the graft or bud is attempted, but there are cases with fruit tree grafts where a mature specimen can simply split off cleanly from the rootstock for no apparent reason. Fortunately, such cases are relatively rare and should not prevent new graft combinations from being attempted. In cases where incompatability prevents what would otherwise be a very happy relation-ship, an **interstock** can be used. An interstock is a scion used to bridge the gap between two incompatible plants. Obviously the interstock must come from a plant that is compatible with the other two partners in the union.

Pomatoes   A truly fascinating exploration of the potential of intergeneric grafting is to put a tomato scion onto a potato rootstock. Since the potato (*Solanum tuberosum*) and the tomato (*Lycopersicon esculentum*) both belong to the same family (Solanaceae), they are fairly closely related and are graft compatible. Mature specimens have been produced at the world famous East Malling Research Station in England, where extensive research on grafting has been carried out for many years.

CHAPTER 10

Plant Tissue Culture or Micropropagation

Most methods of plant propagation can be traced back hundreds and in some cases thousands of years, perhaps because it is an art which is so basic to human civilisation. One technique which does not fit into this scenario is plant tissue culture, sometimes known as micropropagation because of the size of the plant material used as propagules. Plant tissue culture can be defined as the culture of plant material on a sterile nutrient medium. Usually this is done in some sort of glass or plastic vessel which is incubated in a strictly controlled environment under artificial lighting, temperature and humidity control.

Prolific Paws   Tissue culture often seems to capture the imagination of propagators learning about it for the first time. The idea of being able to go from one plant to hundreds of thousands in a space of months is certainly a powerful one. If one has the space and resources in a laboratory, the sky is the limit as far as multiplication of plant material goes. For instance, with kangaroo paws, plants ideally suited to this method, a multiplication rate of four times per month can be achieved. If multiplication of one plant continued unhindered for a full 12 months we would have something like 15 million plants.

■ **Medium:** The sterile nutrient medium which fills the bottom of the container is perhaps the most vital factor in micropropagation and, in particular, the plant hormones or growth regulators used are vital to achieving the desired result. There are numerous media formulations for different species. Media will also vary according to whether we are trying to achieve shoot multiplication or root formation. This complex subject is covered in detail in the theory section of this chapter. It is possible to purchase ready-to-mix sachets of powdered media in order to avoid large capital outlays on laboratory-grade chemicals.

- **Container:** A wide variety of container types can be used. For most media-making systems the containers have to go through an autoclave where they are sterilised at 121 degrees Celsius and under fairly high pressure. Containers must therefore be made of sturdy material such as glass or polycarbonate plastic. Large round polypropylene take-away food containers are used quite successfully for large-scale and small-scale commercial production. Lids may be the snap-on or screw cap type, and some plants such as orchids also require a ventilation hole, which is plugged with sterile cotton wool to prevent contamination.

- **Method:** Basically micropropagation, as the name suggests, entails taking very small pieces of plant tissue and growing them under sterile conditions. The first step is to select the best type of tissue (known as the 'explant') for the particular purpose. For multiplying outstanding clones, this means taking a small piece of the shoot tip or apical meristem and embedding it slightly on the surface of the medium. To render the tip sterile, a section about 1 centimetre long is removed from the shoot tip. This is then placed in a jar of sterilant (usually a solution of sodium hypochlorite or bleach made up to contain 1 per cent available chlorine) containing a couple of drops of detergent to enable even wetting of the surface. Ordinary laundry bleach can be used at a dilution rate of 1 part bleach to 3 parts water (assuming it is normal strength of 4 per cent available chlorine). The tip is shaken in this solution for anything from two minutes to an hour, depending on how soft the tissue is. The jar is then taken into a sterile working environment, such as a surface-sterilised sealed glass chamber (a fish tank can be modified for this purpose) or, for large-scale commercial work, a more expensive laminar flow cabinet. Using sterile instruments, a very small piece of the apical meristem is cut out and placed onto the sterile medium. Further details on method are given later in this chapter.

Banksia integrifolia makes an excellent rootstock for other banksia species as well as being an attractive plant in its own right. *Melinda Bargwanna*

- **Propagation environment:** The incubation area of a micropropagation laboratory generally consists of an air-conditioned room which is fitted out with racks of shelves. Each shelf has a bank of single or double cool white fluorescent lights mounted about 20 to 30 centimetres above it. Temperatures are regulated to approximately 25 degrees Celsius and lights are turned on for 12 to 16 hours per day. Some variations in incubation conditions have proven useful for certain species, but the general guidelines given are adequate for most situations.
- **Time of year:** Micropropagation can be carried out all year round which is one of the major advantages of the technique.
- **Things to look for in the stock plant:** Since the initial explant from the stock plant can potentially give rise to hundreds of thousands of plants, it is vital that the material used is of the very highest quality. The identity and superiority of the plant must be beyond question. Indexing for disease-causing organisms, particularly viruses, is sometimes used in large-scale commercial situations to guarantee 'high health' plant material is propagated.

Theory of Plant Tissue Culture/Micropropagation

The history of plant tissue culture goes back to the beginning of the twentieth century, when primitive attempts at sterile culture were attempted with all sorts of weird and wonderful ingredients. Perhaps the first great practical breakthrough was the work of Knudson ('Nonsymbiotic germination of orchid seeds', 1922, see Further Reading), who devised a very simple medium based on various minerals containing calcium, nitrogen and other essential elements to which sucrose and agar were added. The medium used by Knudson is still widely used today by commercial orchid growers, with some modifications for different orchid types.

Another historical breakthrough in plant tissue culture occurred in the 1930s with the culture of callus tissue (clumps of cells with no apparent structure)

Plants with a clumping rhizomatous habit, such as these are ideal candidates for micropropagation. Clockwise from top left: donkey orchid *(Dinris longifolia)*, *Melinda Bargwanna*, fringe lily *(Thysanotus multiflorus)*, Christmas bell *(Blandfordia grandiflora)*, *Melinda Bargwanna*, black kangaroo paw *(Macropidia fuliginosa)*, *Melinda Bargwanna*, have all been highly successful by this method.

and the regeneration of plantlets from that callus. Callus tissue consists of cells which are undifferentiated (that is, they have not differentiated into tissue such as leaf, stem or petal). Callus tissue looks like an amorphous lump of cells. In the early stages of the research on callus culture, there were high hopes that callus cells could be used for mass commercial propagation since, theoretically, each cell could be made to differentiate into a new plant. It was certainly shown to be possible to regenerate plants from single cells in many species. However, the catch for mass propagation is that the plants resulting from those cells quite often are genetically variable from the parent plant. Nonetheless, callus culture has been a very valuable research tool in learning about the control of tissue differentiation in plants. Early experiments proved that various plant growth regulators (sometimes referred to as plant hormones) when present in miniscule amounts in the growing medium were able to 'tell' the callus to form either roots or shoots or remain as undifferentiated tissue. A group of chemicals known as auxins stimulate root initiation, while another group known as cytokinins is responsible for shoot formation. There are complicating factors in some species where the balance between auxins and cytokinins determines the pattern of differentiation.

Futuristic Fusion   A fascinating aspect of callus culture is the fact that undifferentiated cells of different species can be fused together to form 'vegetative hybrids', technically known as **somatic hybrids**, literally meaning hybrids created from vegetative cells. The advantage of this technique is that hybrids can be produced which are not possible by normal sexual methods of plant breeding.

Plant tissue culture is a fascinating method of propagation because it is a variety of many different methods done in miniature—hence the name micropropagation. For instance, many woody plants such as grevilleas or daphnes are propagated by cutting the miniature stems into pieces and then planting them like micro cuttings onto fresh media, while clumping plants which grow from rhizomes, such as kangaroo paws or daylilies, are done by cutting the miniature clumps into pieces, as you would divide a clump from the garden. The great advantage of micropropagation is that because the process is sterile, there is no possibiltiy of disease affecting the plants and virtually 100 per cent success is guaranteed, provided the cultures remain sterile.

Commercial micropropagation

Plant tissue culture was primarily confined to research for many years after its initial discovery. In the 1960s and 1970s, however, commercial micropropagation really began to gather pace, initially with orchid propagation, but then in the 1970s laboratories specialising in other plant types began to spring up all around the world. The advantages of micropropagation are extremely rapid multiplication rates, initial sterility of plantlets (usually meaning freedom from pests and diseases) and clonal reproduction. Phenomenal multiplication rates are often quoted, such as millions of plants being produced from a single plant within a year. Certainly such rates are theoretically posssible for some species, but these claims neglect the logistics of handling such huge numbers of plants, let alone finding a market for them. Indeed, the great advantage of the rapid multiplication achievable by micropropagation is a two-edged sword—the market for a particular plant can rapidly become flooded, especially if several commercial laboratories decide to concentrate on the one product. Because numbers can be so rapidly increased, the extent of any overproduction often does not become apparent until the final product—either a potted plant or cut flower or food crop—finally reaches the marketplace.

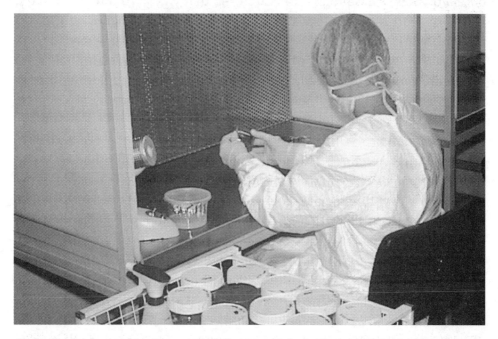

Commercial micropropagation requires the very highest standard of hygiene in order to keep cultures sterile.

The fact that micropropagation is carried out under sterile conditions gives propagators tremendous advantages over conventional methods. Once a plant has been initiated into culture it should be totally sterile and therefore free of any harmful pathogens. It should be pointed out that this is a two-stage process in which the first and rather simple stage is to surface sterilise the plant material and remove the microflora that normally lives in a non-pathogenic way on the surface of the leaves, stems and roots. The second stage, which is not simple and not often practised commercially, is to check the inside of the plant for pathogens by a process called **disease-indexing.** First, sections of plant tissue are placed onto a medium that encourages the growth of a wide range of bacteria and, second, tissue is tested by various advanced methods for the presence of disease-causing viruses. If the material turns out to be contaminated with pathogens, a complicated procedure of culturing microscopic pieces of the growing tip combined with high temperature treatments is used. This has the effect of making the apical tip grow faster than the pathogens can multiply inside the tissue. The process of freeing plants from these disease-causing organisms is an expensive and time-consuming process and is thus normally only done commercially if there is evidence of a problem. The great advantage is that once a plant is disease-free, it can be stored that way in culture indefinitely, and this clean mother stock can be called upon to replenish stock in a conventional propagation programme on a regular basis, say every six to 12 months. The sterile nature of the plant material also means that these plants are much more readily accepted by quarantine authorities world-wide as a means of importing/exporting a particular species.

Micropropagation results in clonal reproduction when the explants used are vegetative structures. (Orchid culture, however, is often done by seed which, of course, will result in genetic variation.) A great advantage of the technique is that it eliminates the need for outdoor beds of mother stock for cuttings etc. This results in great cost savings and removes the headache of constantly having to spray toxic chemicals onto stock plants so that they are free of pests and diseases. This will become increasingly important as more and more toxic chemicals are inevitably withdrawn from the horticultural world over the short and medium-term future.

Micropropagation often results in very bushy, highly branched plants, due to the effects of the relatively high levels of cytokinins used in culture during the multiplication phase. This is usually a great advantage when the plants are grown on, as it eliminates the need for tip pruning, should this be a normal part of the production process. Generally speaking this means a higher quality plant. Plants propagated by this method are also highly suitable for use as mother stock in a conventional propagation programme. For reasons which are not entirely clear, many species are rejuvenated by the micropropagation process. In other words the plants (particularly woody species) switch from the adult stage back to a juvenile stage. The great advantage of this for propagators is that this juvenile material strikes roots much more readily when it is used as cuttings. The effect seems to last for up to six months after plants come out of culture. So even though micro-propagated plants are relatively expensive, this is well justified if they improve the success rate when they are used as the basis for mother stock blocks. In addition, they have the huge advantage of being disease-free (at least in theory).

Grevillea 'Robyn Gordon'

This plant provides a classic example of rejuvenation through micropropagataion. When it first appeared in the 1970s, this exceptionally ornamental grevillea proved very difficult to strike as cuttings, probably because its ever-blooming habit meant that good cutting material was rarely produced. Once it was micropropagated, the resulting juvenile material had a different leaf form and was very shy to flower, as is normal in the juvenile stage of most woody plants. The juvenile material also gave wood which would strike at a rate of about 95 per cent, as opposed to 30–40 per cent in normal adult flowering material. Some propagators 'twigged' to the idea of simply using micropropagated material to produce mother stock plants rather than trying to use these expensive plants for more routine production of plants.

In addition to the tremendous advantages of micropropagation, there are some significant drawbacks. Genetic variability has been an unexpected result of the plant tissue culture process in a number of commercially micro-propagated species. It is an established fact that genetic variability can arise in plant tissue cultures, and this phenomenon has even led to the coining of the scientific term **'somaclonal variation'**, meaning variation derived from somatic (vegetative) cells produced from clonal material. Genetic variability arising within a clone does not just happen in tissue cultures—many new varieties of camellias and other plants have arisen as mutations or 'sports' on plants growing in gardens or pots. What does seem to be a little different about somaclonal variants is that they appear to occur at a higher frequency.

These mutations are often associated with the culture going through a callus stage, and one theory suggests that when a mutation occurs in such undifferentiated cells, each cell has the capacity to give rise to a new plant. If a mutation occurs in a cell within a shoot, as normally happens in sporting, the mutant cell often is swamped by normal cells and does not form a new shoot, let alone a new plant. Some researchers have found somaclonal variation to be of great interest as a potential source of new genetic variability in plant breeding, and research programs have been devised deliberately to try and induce it. However, for commercial micropropagators it could obviously spell disaster if deleterious mutations start cropping up in their production process. The solution for commercial micropropagation appears to lie in avoiding culture systems which involve formation of callus tissue. The alternative is to use systems where shoot multiplication arises from axillary buds only. This can be achieved by carefully regulating the concentrations of auxins and cytokinins used in the multiplication medium. Regular re-initiation of culture, say every six to 12 months, may be needed if problems start to occur. Biochemical techniques such as isoenzyme and DNA analysis also show promise as a way of monitoring long-term genetic stability.

Another major problem in commercial micropropagation has been overproduction. Once the micropropagation of a particular plant species has been perfected, there is a tendency for commercial laboratories to simultaneously pick up on the research and produce large quantities of that plant. Because of the potential for rapidly building up large numbers of small plants, enormous quantities can end up in production nurseries and only a year or so later overproduction becomes apparent. It is therefore advisable for production nurseries to exercise some caution in ordering plants from commercial micropropagation laboratories.

Theoretically, plant tissue culture results in beautiful, disease-free plants, and this is certainly a very achievable result. However, it must not be assumed that every plant that is micropropagated is totally disease-free. Commercial production laboratories often do not routinely index their cultures for diseases during the inititiation stage because of the time and expense involved. In this circumstance it is highly possible for contaminants to survive inside the plant, particularly viruses and bacteria. The ideal conditions provided during micropropagation can sometimes mean that disease symptoms are masked, and it is only after subsequent planting out that problems become evident, usually when the plant is subjected to water or nutritional stress. It is therefore particularly important that users of micropropagated plants be on their guard for such problems and do not automatically assume plants to be disease-free simply because they have been micropropagated.

A rather strange condition that is not uncommon in micropropagation is known by a variety of names—**glassiness, vitrification and hyperhydricity**. The symptoms of the disorder are an opaque, shiny or 'glassy' appearance to the leaves and stems, and collapse of the plants when they are transplanted into the greenhouse. It is thought to be due to changes in the structure of the plant's cells which cause weakening of the cell wall and subsequent absorption of excessive amounts of water. It can be overcome by treating the plants while they are still in culture by cooling the base of the container they are in (or stopping it warming up too much), and by increasing the level of the gelling agent in the medium, normally agar, to produce a harder gel that reduces water uptake by the plant.

Plant Tissue Culture as a Research Tool

A fascinating aspect of plant tissue culture is its use as a research tool. Various techniques and their applications are discussed below.

Embryo and ovule culture
This technique involves the extraction and culturing of embryos and ovules (developing seeds). There are numerous reasons for using this technique, many of which revolve around plant breeding programmes. Often when distantly related species are hybridised in a breeding programme, a viable embryo is produced but seed does not develop because the food source (or endosperm) aborts. By culturing the embryo, a viable plant develops and some very interesting new hybrids have been produced which would be

impossible without tissue culture. Another advantage of this technique is that embryos germinate immediately and are not subject to seed dormancy, which may be characteristic of a particular species. Also, once the embryo develops it can be multiplied so that instead of having a single plant the breeder can produce any number desired for the purposes of trialling. Yet another feature of this method is that a number of species mature more quickly once they have been planted out of culture, and instead of waiting years for the seedling to flower, it may happen in months. I have observed this in Geraldton wax (*Chamelaucium* species) and kangaroo paws (*Anigozanthos* species), and have no doubt that it would apply to many other plant groups.

Anther culture

Anthers represent the male organs of flowers, as they bear the pollen used to fertilise the female parts (carpels). The pollen grains in the anther are induced to multiply and can usually be persuaded to differentiate into whole plants. The interesting thing about pollen cells is that they have half the normal chromosome number and thus the plants derived from them also have only half the normal number. They are known as haploids, and are remarkable for the fact that they have only a single set of chromosomes (i.e., the males ones) instead of the paired sets found in a normal plant, which are derived from the male and female sets being brought together during sexual reproduction. Since they don't have paired chromosomes and cannot form viable pollen or ovules at meiosis (the process in which each pair of chromosomes in an organism splits, with one of each pair going to the pollen or ovules), haploids are sterile. You may be wondering what use it is to plant breeders to produce this sterile haploid. The answer lies in the fact that the chromosome number of the sterile haploid can be doubled using the chemical colchicine. This means that an exact replica of each chromosome is formed. Colchicine acts by preventing the formation of new cell walls in another process of cell division known as mitosis—that is, the chromosomes reproduce themselves normally and go to each end of the cell, but a new cell wall does not form, resulting in one cell with double the chromosome number. Each of these new cells now has paired sets of chromosomes with each pair identical (in other words, they are homozygous). The plant can now undergo meiosis normally, meaning that fertility has been restored. Not only is fertility restored, but because the pollen and ovules produced are all identical, the plant is completely true breeding. This greatly speeds up plant breeding programmes as the breeder knows exactly what the genetic makeup of the plants is and can be confident that there are no unwanted hidden (recessive) characteristics that will surface in later generations.

Protoplast culture

A protoplast is basically a cell without its cell wall. Protoplasts are created by taking a callus cell culture and introducing the enzyme cellulase which dissolves the cell wall. The cells then continue to proliferate without their cell walls. Protoplasts are of great interest to plant breeders because they can be used for some rather interesting genetic manipulation techniques. Protoplast fusion is, as the name suggests, a process where the membranes around the protoplasts are disrupted and then different protoplasts fuse together. The technique is used to create hybrids between species that cannot be hybridised by normal sexual means. This application of protoplast fusion is known as somatic (vegetative) hybridisation. It is often used to obtain hybrids between different genera, for instance a cross has been obtained between tomatoes and potatoes. Protoplast cultures are also used

Liquid nitrogen is used for cryogenic storage of tissue cultures of endangered plant species from Western Australia at Kings Park Botanic Gardens.

in genetic engineering techniques, where fragments of DNA containing specific genes are able to be inserted into protoplasts of various species.

Callus culture

As noted earlier, a callus culture contains undifferentiated cells—in other words, the cells are not part of any discernible organ such as a leaf, stem or root. Callus cultures can be maintained for months or even years and still maintain the capacity to regenerate into whole plants. Another interesting facet of callus cultures is that a high rate of genetic mutations is normally observed in plants regenerated from them. This unexpected source of variability is of some interest to plant breeders, and is treated in more detail in the section on somaclonal variation (the name coined to describe the phenomenon) earlier in this chapter.

Stages of Micropropagation

It is useful to divide the micropropagation process into various stages so that the various operations involved can be better understood. Those stages are:

0. Preparation of the stock plant for initiation
1. Initiation of cultures
2. Shoot multiplication
3. Root initiation
4. Planting out into the greenhouse, i.e. removal from the sterile nutrient medium.

Stage 0

This stage involves growing the stock plant in a relatively clean medium (e.g. pure perlite) in order to reduce the load of micro-organisms. In addition, overhead watering of the stock plant is avoided and a regular programme of fungicides is used to help reduce microbial populations. The stock plant should also be grown in a protected environment such as a glasshouse to give the propagator better control of the conditions.

Stage 1

Involves the initiation of the sterile culture. Any plant in a greenhouse or outdoor environment will have a rather extensive array of microbes growing on its surface and sometimes inside it as well. The objective of stage 1 is to try to completely eliminate this microflora. Sterilising the plant tissue presents some difficulties as one has to kill the cells of the microbes while keeping enough of the plant cells alive to allow the plant to continue growing. The usual treatments involve soaking the explant in a sterilant such as sodium or calcium hypochlorite bleach. These are not the only sterilants available, but they are certainly the most commonly used ones. In order to make sure that the sterilant comes into full contact with every part of the tissue surface, wetting agents are also used. A short soak (30 to 60 seconds) in 70 per cent alcohol serves this purpose, as does the addition of a few drops of detergent to the sterilising solution. The length of time in the sterilant depends on the type of explant used—if well protected tissue such as the seed is used it can be sterilised for an hour or more, but if soft tissue such as an active shoot tip is used, the time should be cut to one to five minutes. Once the explant has been sterilised, it can be rinsed in sterile water a couple of times before being placed on the sterile medium, although I have had considerable success omitting this final step.

A crucial factor in the success of stage 1 is in the selection of the best tissue for use as the explant. If the objective of the exercise does not involve clonal propagation, seed is the easiest tissue to start with as it normally has a tough seed coat protecting the embryo, which is usually sterile if the seed coat is intact. If clonal propagation is desired, the best option is normally an organised meristem such as an axillary or apical bud. These structures are best because they minimise the possibility of genetic variability (somaclonal variation). Normally a hormone-free medium is used for stage 1.

The sterility of the explant is initially assessed visually. Fungal contamination is normally obvious within a few days of initiation, as the culture rapidly becomes enveloped by a mass of fungal hyphae which usually resmembles cotton wool and is clearly visible with the naked eye. Bacterial contamination is often much harder to spot. It will sometimes be manifested by shiny raised colonies on the surface of the medium or enveloping the explant. Bacterial growth shows up at the submerged base of the explant as a halo, which can be seen when the medium is held up to a light source. Often these haloes are very faint and considerable skill is needed to spot them. Bacterial haloes can take many weeks or even months to develop and this can create considerable problems. It is thought by many researchers that these haloes develop from bacteria that are inside the plant tissue, which could explain the long lead times in their development. An alternative approach to visual assessment is the indexing of the cultures by placing the apparently sterile explants onto a nutrient medium that favours the growth of bacteria. There are a number of choices for such a medium and a detailed treatment of this can be found in any good microbiology textbook. I have found potato dextrose agar to be useful for indexing a wide range of plants. It should be noted that indexing does not guarantee sterility, although it can be considered an excellent guide.

Stage 2

Involves the rapid shoot multiplication stage of the process. Assuming that stage 1 has successfully produced a sterile culture, the resulting explant can then be moved onto a multiplication medium. The critical ingredient of most if not all multiplication media is one of the cytokinin group of plant hormones. The most commonly used cytokinins are benzyl amino purine (BAP) and kinetin at concentrations ranging from 0.01 to 10 milligrams per litre of medium. Sometimes auxins such as naphthalene acetic acid (NAA) or indole butyric acid (IBA) are also added, usually at concentrations of one tenth to one half of the cytokinin concentration. There can be no doubt that the cytokinins are the most important factor in breaking down apical dominance and encouraging masses of axillary shoots such that the culture often resembles a miniature forest with shoots too numerous to count.

It may take a few months for the culture to reach a good multiplication rate, as the hormone treatments sometimes take time to alter the physiological state of the plant, particularly in woody species. One should also be aware that over time the multiplication rate may become too great and the resulting plantlets too prolific. In such cases, when the plantlets are planted out in the greenhouse they continue to produce masses of axillary shoots and flowering can be delayed. This is a significant problem for commercial growers of cut flowers or flowering pot plants. Usually the plants grow out of the condition and go on to flower normally but even if this is the case the grower has lost valuable growing space while waiting for flowering to occur. If such overabundant proliferation occurs, the answer is often to lower the level of cytokinins in the stage 2 medium. It may even be necessary to put the cultures onto a hormone-free medium until they assume a more sustainable multiplication level. In some rare cases this problem is due to a genetic mutation and the plants do not grow out of the condition. It is a

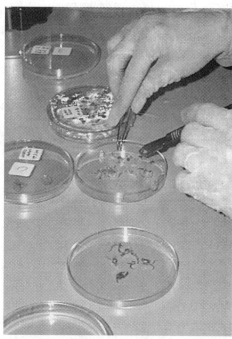

Anticlockwise from top right: The process of subculturing requires nimble fingers; a standard incubation area for stage 2; a stage 2 culture of Geraldton wax *(Chamelaucium uncinatum)*—note the lack of roots; a stage 3 of Geralton wax after removal from flask.

good strategy to regularly grow out a sample of your micropropagated stock to flowering stage to check that there are no obvious mutations.

The process whereby the multiplying cultures are divided is known as sub-culturing and the methods used will depend on the type of plant being cultured. For many woody plants such as grevilleas, the stems are simply cut into sections consisting of two or three nodes and these are then placed on the medium like a miniature cutting. For clumping plants such as kangaroo paws and gerberas, the clumps of shoots are cut into sections, as though one was doing the process of division in miniature. For other herbaceous species such as African violets and cape violets (*Streptocarpus*) that are normally multiplied by leaf cuttings, miniature leaf sections can be used and these can be as small as you like as there is no danger of diseases rotting away the small pieces of tissue as often happens in the greenhouse with leaf cuttings. As you can see, the micropropagator can gain many clues by researching the conventional propagation technique for the particular species they are working on.

Stage 3

Involves the initiation of roots while the plants are still in sterile culture. For some species this stage can be eliminated by planting stage 2 material straight into the greenhouse. Generally speaking, this method is only satisfactory for species that form roots very easily, such as Boston ferns and African violets. For the majority of species that are commercially micropropagated stage 3 is virtually essential. The rapidly multiplying shoots from stage 2 cultures are cut into individual plantlets, and then planted onto a suitable medium with the base of the plantlet just submerged in the medium. The stage 3 (rooting) medium usually contains one or more auxins as the active ingredient(s) for the initiation of roots. Indole butyric acid (IBA) or naphthalene acetic acid (NAA) are the two most common choices.

Stage 3 media are usually agar based and are therefore solid in nature, although some success has been achieved using liquid media. (It is thought that chemicals exuded by the plant that may inhibit root formation do not build up around the base of the plantlet as they do on an agar based medium.) Where a solid medium is used, an alternative is to incorporate activated charcoal in the medium as it is thought to absorb inhibitory chemicals. If liquid media are being used, some sort of support such as a wedge of filter paper to suspend the plantlet is used so that the newly forming root system is able to obtain plenty of oxygen.

Ideally plantlets are left on the stage 3 medium only until roots are just visible. This makes for much easier handling of the plantlets when they are transferred to the greenhouse, and results in less shock and therefore more rapid acclimatisation to greenhouse conditions.

Stage 4

Involves the transfer of plants from the sterile tissue culture container to the non-sterile greenhouse environment. This stage often presents major difficulties for plant propagators for a number of reasons. The success or otherwise of this stage is often the factor which determines whether a particular species can be viable for commercial micropropagation.

There are several reasons why tissue cultured plants are difficult to transfer to the greenhouse environment. During incubation they are grown under relatively low light intensities which do not support significant levels of photosynthesis. The plant's energy requirements are met instead by the supply of sucrose (sugar) that is an ingredient of most media. Thus once it is planted out, the plantlet takes some time before it starts to become self-sufficient. In addition, the environment in the culture vessel is one of very high humidity, as evidenced by the condensation normally visible on the inside of the vessel. The tissue cultured plants adapt to this very high humidity by leaving their stomates (the pores in the leaf which allow exchange of gases with the atmosphere) almost permanently open. Presumably this occurs because the leaf has no need to close the stomates as the plant is never under water stress in the vessel. It takes some time for stomatal function to be regained once the plant is in the greenhouse. The surface of the leaf itself also tends to be different in the tissue culture environment, as the normal waxy cuticle that forms on most leaves does not develop again, also presumably because there is less need for the leaf to prevent water loss.

Gradual acclimatisation is required to overcome these three factors, otherwise the plant will be very susceptible to water stress and may easily die in the first week or two after transfer to the greenhouse. Indeed, the safest course of action is to wait until new leaf and root growth has begun in the greenhouse before removing the plantlets from the hardening off area.

Let us now look at the requirements for the hardening off area for stage 4 cultures. Obviously the conditions should initially be similar to the conditions in the incubation stage, namely very high humidity, low light levels and moderate temperature levels. Greenhouse areas with misting or fogging units are a useful starting point. However, on their own they are often not the ideal for all species. The use of a humidity tent in addition to fogging or misting often gives a margin for error in maintaining more consistent humidity levels. Micropropagated plantlets represent an extremely high investment and therefore I would suggest that the extra expense of a humidity tent is well and truly justified if large quantities of micropropagated plants are to be handled. The tent can be gradually opened up over a period of a fortnight or so and the misting or fogging gradually reduced. Temperaure control in the hardening off area is also of paramount importance. This can be achieved in a number of ways that can be found in any good book on greenhouse design or management.

The actual process of planting out stage 4 cultures is particularly critical to ensuring a high success rate. The plantlets are at their most vulnerable as they are removed from the flask. This is perhaps the softest plant material that a propagator will ever handle, given its lack of cuticle and stomatal function. The material must be handled quickly, and generally it is removed from the flask and placed into warm water to try to loosen the jelly-like medium at the base of the culture. It is advisable to remove as much of this gel as possible as it will encourage the growth of fungi and bacteria around the base of the plant. Usually these microbes are not harmful to the plant but if present in large amounts they can tend to smother it with their vigorous growth.

Planting out of cultures is often done in the humidity tent or misting area to minimise the chances of the plantlets drying out. Antitranspirant sprays are sometimes used to good effect at this stage—these are sprays that put a polymer coating on the surface of the leaves and dramatically reduce water loss. Once the stage 4 plants have been hardened off for a few weeks, new leaf growth can be expected and at this point they are ready to be moved to a different environment such as a shadehouse.

Dwarf mutations of *Lisianthus russellianus* from plant tissue culture have been selected for pot plant culture.

Micropropagation media

The medium is a crucial factor in achieving the required result for each of the stages of the micropropagation process. The major components of the various media used in plant tissue culture and their function is as follows:

1. **Mineral nutrients:** Usually all the essential elements for plant growth are included in the medium, namely the so-called macronutrients (required in relatively large amounts)—nitrogen, phosphorus, potassium, magnesium, calcium, sulphur—and the micronutrients or trace elements —iron, molybdenum, manganese, copper, zinc, boron and chlorine. Normally these nutrients are provided at fairly high levels. It may be worth experimenting to find the level of various nutrients to suit the requirements of particular species. For instance, *Grevillea* 'Robyn Gordon' benefits from a large reduction in phosphorus levels and elevation of iron levels.

2. **Sugars:** The relatively low light intensities used in the incubation of tissue cultures means that levels of photosynthesis are fairly negligible and insufficient to support plant growth. Accordingly, an energy source to fuel growth is provided in the form of sucrose or glucose. For most media, ordinary household sugar can be used. Levels of sucrose can be varied to achieve different objectives. For instance, elevated levels of sucrose of 60 to 90 grams ;per litre are used to encourage the formation of bulbs and corms in culture for plants such as gladiolus and tulips. Usually between 20 to 40 grams per litre are added to the medium.

3. **Agar or other gelling agent:** Agar is an extract of seaweed that melts when it is heated and then solidifies at room temperature. Its purpose is to solidify the medium, thereby enabling plants to stand upright—in other words to provide support. The major drawback with agar is that it gives the medium a cloudy appearance which makes it very difficult to spot microbial contaminants growing on the base of the cultures. To over-come this problem there are alternatives to agar, e.g. Gel-rite, that behave in the same way as agar but give a perfectly clear gel. The significantly higher cost of these clear gelling agents has meant that agar is usually still the preferred gelling agent for many laboratories. Gel-rite is, however, often used in stage 1 media for initiation of cultures, given its better

Micropropagation is an extremely useful tool to rapidly multiply new cultivars of various plants such as gladiolus, top left and right, *Fred Meyer*; and daylily *(Hemerocallis). Melinda Bargwanna* capacity to reveal contaminants. The concentration of gelling agent used in the medium is very important. If the gel is too hard, it makes insertion of cultures difficult and it also slows down the rate at which chemicals can move through the medium. On the other hand if the gel is too soft, it will not support the plant material. Different brands of agar and alternative gelling agents have variable gelling characteristics. A concentration of 7–8 grams per litre of agar should give a reasonable gel strength for most brands.

4. **Vitamins and other growth factors:** Various complex organic chemicals are used routinely in media as they have been found to be beneficial for a number of species. These include thiamine, nicotinic acid, pyridoxine, inositol, pantothenic acid, biotin and riboflavin. The actual role of these chemicals is often not clear, but they probably assist growth by supplementing the complex biochemicals that are normally synthesised by the plant as a consequence of photosynthesis. Another role could be in interactions with plant growth regulators, as riboflavin has been shown to have dramatic effects on the response to cytokinins and auxins of *Eriostemon australasius* cultures.

5. **Plant growth regulators:** Arguably this is the most important ingredient in achieving successful micropropagation. Cytokinins are used to induce

Analytical balances are required to accurately weigh very tiny quantities of plant growth regulators.

multiple shoot formation while auxins are used for root initiation. Cytokinins most commonly used are BAP (benzyl amino purine) and kinetin (furfuryl amino purine), at concentrations ranging from 0.01 to 10 milligrams per litre. Other cytokinins exist and are used occasionally but not regularly because of their higher cost. These include zeatin (hydroxy methyl butenyl amino purine), IPA or 2-IP (isopentenyl amino purine) and PBA (benzyl amino tetra hydro pyranyl purine). Cytokinin solutions are prepared by dissolving the powdered chemical in a very small amount of fairly dilute hydrochloric acid and then adding water to make it up to the required concentration. Auxins most commonly used are NAA (naphthalene acetic acid) and IBA (indole butyric acid) at concentrations ranging from 0.1 to 10 milligrams per litre. Auxin solutions are prepared by dissolving the powdered auxin in a very small amount of alcohol and then adding water to make it up to the required concentration. Other auxins that have been used from time to time include IAA (indole acetic acid) and 2,4-D (dichlorophenoxy acetic acid). Gibberellins are used at times as a means of breaking dormancy in shoots, bulbs and corms that are being initiated into culture.

6. **Other additives:** Over the years various complex substances have been added, with the most common being coconut milk and banana pulp, particularly for orchid culture. These additives obviously would supply a whole range of nutrients generally needed by plants and in particular both substances are known to be a crude source of cytokinins. Both additives are used at a rate of approximately 10–15 per cent by volume. Yeast extract and casein hydrolysate are also used at times, and these are known to be a source of amino acids and vitamins.

References for commonly used micropropagation media (such as Murashige and Skoog) are given in 'Futher Reading' at the end of this book.

Micropropagation at home

Large scale commercial micropropagation requires laboratory conditions to achieve the levels of hygiene and sterility necessary for profitable operation. However, if one is prepared to accept lower but still acceptable success levels, then it is certainly possible to improvise and establish a small micropropagation facility in a garage or kitchen situation. Many orchid propagation nurseries operate in this sort of environment.

An ordinary kitchen pressure cooker can be used to sterilise media and instruments, instead of large and very expensive autoclaves. To ensure that you have sterilised materials sufficiently you can obtain autoclave tape that changes colour when sufficient treatment has been applied. A sterile micro-environment can be created for transfer of sterile cultures using a fish tank that is enclosed on all sides and has small holes created to allow access for the operator's arms. The open side of the tank can be enclosed with tough plastic. To lessen the cost of media-making, ready-made mixtures of standard formulae can be purchased (see details in Appendix 3). These mixes come in pre-prepared sachets which make up convenient quantities of media, such as one or ten litre batches. The mixes can be bought with hormones already added, or hormone-free. It is often better to use the latter and add your own blends of cytokinins and auxins to give maximum flexibility. A number of universities offer courses in micropropagation and these can be well worthwhile for the budding micropropagator. Another excellent resource is Ron de Fossard's *Plant Tissue Culture for Plant Propagators* (see Further Reading), which includes an extensive set of colour slides accompanying the manual on the practical aspects of micropropagation. Specialist horticultural libraries should have this kit or be able to obtain it on inter-library loan.

CHAPTER 11

Stock Plant Management

One of the most basic considerations in plant propagation is the judicious management of the plants which will supply the propagation material. It does not matter whether we are talking about cuttings, micropropagation, grafting or division, if the stock plants are not kept in optimum condition, the efficiency of propagation will rapidly decline. There are several crucial facets of stock plant management to consider, including nutrition, management of pests and diseases, genetic stability and juvenility (or physiological state). In commercial situations, the ideal is to have stock plants in a greenhouse equipped to allow manipulation of temperature, humidity, ventilation, watering, fertilising and daylength.

Nutrition

Stock plants need a well balanced diet if they are to produce good quality propagules. The optimum balance of nutrients will vary from species to species, so a little research will be required on the part of the propagator. For most species a complete fertiliser, i.e. one containing all the essential macro and micro nutrients necessary for plant growth, will be sufficient. Various proprietary brands are available such as Aquasol, Thrive and Zest, which will all be excellent for the task. Generally fertiliser will be applied generously during the early part of a growing season to stimulate a good flush of new growth. Fertilising can often be used to manipulate growth through the year. If it is possible to also control temperature we can often force growth at a time of year when it would not normally occur by applying fertiliser. Generally speaking liquid fertilisers will give much quicker responses and thereby allow more flexibility. Care should be taken to avoid excessive use of fertilisers in which nitrogen is dominant. While such fertilisers will usually give a surge of growth, the resulting material may be a little weak and will not make ideal propagation material.

Management of pests and diseases

This is perhaps the most difficult facet of stock plant maintenance. Every species has its own characteristic set of problems and it is almost impossible to eradicate all of them. The objective should be to keep the problems to the absolute minimum through whatever means are feasible (see box below on integrated pest and disease management). A most difficult aspect is the problems that cannot be detected by the human eye, in particular, virus diseases. Viruses are so tiny that an electron microscope is needed to see them. Indeed they are so small that it is difficult to distinguish features that could be used to identify them. As a result, classification of viruses does not follow the normal scientific convention for naming organisms, namely the binomial system where a genus and species name is given. Instead viruses are described in terms of the organism they infect and the symptoms they cause, for example, cucumber mosaic virus. For the propagator, viruses present a nasty problem as their diagnosis is rather difficult and their eradication even more so. In recent times diagnosis of viruses has become much easier through the development of various new technologies.

By far the best approach to pest and diseases is to exclude them from the mother stock in the first place. The first and most vital factor is to start with disease-indexed mother stock, normally achieved by using such stock grown from micropropagation (see section in Chapter 10). This mother stock needs to go into an area that has been adequately prepared for such clean material—it should be free of weeds that may harbour pests and diseases. The growing medium should preferably be pasteurised or fumigated. Insect proof screens can be used to prevent the entry of virus-carrying insects such as thrips. Keep traffic (both human and machine) to the absolute minimum and use sterilant foot baths for staff entering and leaving the propagation area. A programme of active measures such as biological controls, and pesticides and fungicides where appropriate, will also be necessary (see box on integrated pest and disease management below). It will not always be possible to implement all these measures. However, the good news is that the effect of these practices is additive—in other words, each measure that is implemented will help to achieve the overall goal of minimising pests and diseases.

Integrated Pest and Disease Management (IPDM) in Chrysanthemum Mother Stock: A Case Study

IPDM is all about reducing our reliance on toxic chemicals to control pests and diseases. It refers to the use of all possible methods of minimising economic damage to plants by using whatever means available, whether they be cultural, biological or chemical. The author has recently been involved in a pilot study using IPDM principles to manage chrysanthemum mother stock for cutting production for cut flowers. The lynch pin for the project was the use of a variety of beneficial organisms to control the numerous pests that seem to be drawn to chrysanthemum like a magnet. Initial planting stock was obtained from disease-indexed micropropagated plants, which provided very vigorous clean planting stock.

- Two-spotted (red spider) mite is perhaps the worst pest of chrysanthemums in greenhouse production. It was managed by means of a predatory mite, *Phytoseiulus persimilis*, which attacks not only two-spotted mite but also bean spider mite and bamboo mite. Regular monitoring of the undersurface of the leaves is essential. As soon as pests are noticed, the predators should be introduced.
- Whitefly was controlled by means of a parasitic wasp, *Encarsia formosa*, which was introduced to the stock on a weekly basis by means of small cards with parasitised whitefly eggs attached. The wasp emerges from the eggs and promptly goes forth to find more eggs to parasitise.
- Caterpillars were controlled by regular use of a bacterial pathogen, *Bacillus thuringiensis*. This organism is totally non-toxic to all but the larvae of lepidopterous insects, namely moths and butterflies. It is available under various brand names such as Delfin®. It is sprayed onto the plants and the caterpillar must ingest, it so it is important to get as good a coverage of the foliage as possible.
- Thrips can be a problem in shoot tips and later on in the flowers. New predators are likely to become available in the immediate future. Again, the plants need to be regularly monitored for thrips, and predators introduced as soon as they are noticed.
- Fungus gnat is a pest that produces larvae that attack the roots and

can burrow into the bottom of the stem and chew out the inside (see Chapter 13 on pests and diseases). A beneficial nematode is available that can be drenched onto the soil either with a watering can or through a drip irrigation system.

■ Fungal diseases can also be a problem in chrysanthemum, with the most important being white rust. Fortunately most beneficial organisms are fairly tolerant of most fungicides, so a programme of fungicides is usually compatible with IPDM programmes.

Regular monitoring of the project was essential, not only to determine when to introduce beneficials, but also when to 'spot spray' any patches of pests that were getting out of control. In such cases, chemical controls were used in very small areas to assist the beneficial organisms in maintaining control. Blanket spraying of most chemicals often results in damage to the beneficials (although there are a few compatible chemicals which suppliers of beneficial organisms can advise on).

See Appendix 3 for details of commercial suppliers of beneficial insects and mites.

Genetic stability

One of the greatest problems in plant propagation is in maintaining genetically stability, or 'trueness-to-type'. In other words, when a plant has been selected as being superior and subsequently cloned by various asexual means such as cuttings or layering, it may sometimes be subject to genetic variation (or simple mix-ups of different varieties), which of course defeats the purpose of propagating it vegetatively. The most obvious cause of problems is mistaken identity due to poor labelling, or use of mother stock that has not been positively identified. Such problems are easily fixed by better organisation and sound propagation 'housekeeping'. A couple of useful suggestions include the use of tie-on aluminium labels, which are effectively 'engraved' when they are written on with reasonable pressure. If mother stock is to be kept in pots, the label should be written directly onto the side of the pot with a paint pen or some other type of permanent marker.

The more difficult but fortunately less likely cause is genetic mutation of the mother stock. Such mutations are known as 'sports' and usually do not have any obvious cause. Genetic variations may not always be obvious at first and can affect various characteristics, such as growth habit and the morphology of the leaves and flowers. The best way to guard against such problems is to regularly grow on a sample of the finished product to a mature plant, to ensure it has all the correct characteristics. More sophisticated, but expensive, methods of 'genetic fingerprinting' are available at institutions such as universities. Such methods are financially justifiable in commercial situations, where hundreds of thousands of plants are concerned. Particular care should be taken with plants produced by micro-propagation as their cultivar is very difficult to identify when they are still in sterile culture, due to the minute size of the leaves and the absence of flowers. Of course, 'sports' have long been a source of new cultivars, particularly when variation occurs in the flower, but it must be recognised that variations can be undesirable.

Astute management of pests and diseases is crucial for intensive crops like chrysanthemum.

Sports and the Role of Genetic Mutations in Producing New Varieties

A **bud sport** is a genetic mutation that occurs in the shoot tip of a plant and then grows out so that a whole section of the original plant is genetically different. When this occurs it is possible to find several different flower types on the one plant. Bud sports can be propagated vegetatively by cuttings or aerial layering and may be subsequently stabilised as new cultivars in their own right. Indeed, there are camellia varieties that are well known for their capacity to sport and some, such as *Camellia japonica* 'Aspasia', have given rise to a whole family of new cultivars. The original cultivar, which arose in the garden of Camden Park, New South Wales in the 1840s, was named by William Macarthur and has creamy white petals with streaks of pink. Sports that have been derived from it have similar flower form but differ in colour, and include 'Lady Loch' (light pink, deep pink streaks), 'Otahu Beauty' (red), 'Camden Park' (red with white streaks) and 'Strawberry Blonde' (salmon pink, deep pink streaks). Sports occur when a genetic mutation happens in the shoot tip during the normal cell division that results from mitosis. Mutations can be at several levels, from changes in single genes to changes in whole chromosomes, or even doubling of chromosome number when a new cell wall fails to form properly between two newly divided cells. The reasons why sports occur spontaneously in garden plants is not clear, but certainly there are several methods that can be used to induce sports artificially. These include irradiation of plants or even cuttings with x-rays or gamma rays, or treatment with mutagenic chemicals such as colchicine, which is known to cause doubling of chromosome numbers.

Juvenility

Woody plants go through stages of maturation, just as humans do, with a juvenile stage followed by an intermediate stage leading to full sexual maturity in the adult phase. The various stages are often accompanied by very distinct changes in the appearance of the plant. These changes are very often also associated with a dramatic change in the ability of the wood to form roots when it is used for cuttings. This has been observed in woody plants as diverse as conifers (e.g. Douglas fir), deciduous species such as apples and pears, and evergreens such as the eucalypts. The eucalypts, in fact, provide one of the best examples of this pattern.

The juvenile stage in many eucalypts is characterised by round bluish foliage which gradually elongates to the long, thin sickle-shaped leaves which we mostly associate with gum trees. There appear to be a couple of reasons why juvenile wood is easier to strike than adult. In eucalypts unidentified root-inhibiting chemicals have been found in various species. The same chemicals were absent in easily-rooted seedling (juvenile) material from a wide range of species. In addition, plants in the juvenile phase generally (although not always) do not have the capacity to flower. Flowering is known to be associated with changes that are not conducive to adventitious root formation in of woody plants.

The really fascinating thing about this topic is that adult plants can often be rejuvenated by very hard pruning. When stock plants are to be managed for cuttings, a technique known as 'hedging' or 'coppicing' is used in which the plants are regularly pruned back to ground level or just above. In plants which are capable of rejuvenation, this results in vigorous juvenile regrowth which is highly suitable for cutting material. An 'orchard' of stock plants used only for cutting production is desirable, as coppicing does not give a particularly ornamental result in most cases. Sanitation and hygiene are also critical in such orchards, as large wounds are created by coppicing established trees and shrubs. A very wide range of woody plants can be manipulated in this way, and a very good indication of the success of the technique is whether the species normally responds well to hard pruning. If it does, it is very likely a candidate for **rejuvenation**.

Another option for rejuvenation is to use recently propagated material, particularly micropropagated plantlets which have recently been hardened off. The micropropagation process generally utilises plant growth regulators such as cytokinins, which appear to have the effect of rejuvenating the plant. The plants can be potted up or grown in specially prepared beds, and will give excellent cutting material for many months. This has been observed by the author in a wide range of species. Even when woody plants are propagated by standard cutting methods, there is often some degree of rejuvenation and it is often worth renewing mother stock on a six to 12 monthly basis to take advantage of this **juvenility effect**.

Eucalyptus Hedges

Because of the difficulty encountered in their vegetative propagation, eucalypts have traditionally been propagated from seed. The application of mother stock management has dramatically altered this situation in the last decade. Eucalyptus is an extremely important genus for wood production and is probably the most widely planted tree type in the world. Seed propagation results in enormous genetic variability in the progeny. Methods for the production of cuttings led to trial work with vegetatively propagated eucalypts in various parts of the world during the 1970s. Plantings of cutting-grown eucalypts in the Congo in Africa and in Espirito Santo State in Brazil resulted in a doubling in growth in plantations, with the gain being mainly attributed to the genetic superiority of the plants, and minor improvement being due to better growing practices. In Brazil, the Aracruz Celulose S.A. company perfected vegetative propagation on a commercial scale and by 1990 the company was raising about 50 million rooted cuttings per year.

The techniques to produce such massive amounts of cuttings are as follows. Stock plants are produced by selecting superior parent trees from plantations and propagating them by one of several methods—grafting onto juvenile rootstocks, aerial layering or coppicing the trees, and taking cuttings of the vigorous juvenile regrowth. Hedges of the superior stock are planted and harvested as new growth is produced. The trick is to keep taking the cuttings as the new growth is produced, in order to maintain the juvenile state of the stock plants. Cuttings are taken and prepared by standard methods using 1–3 per cent IBA and set in a very simple shadehouse environment with intermittent misting. Another key to successful production is to ruthlessly discard poor-rooting clones.

(See further *Eucalypt Domestication and Breeding* by K. Eldridge, J Davidson, C. Harwood and G. van Wyk, Oxford Science Publications, 1994.)

Flowering status

As a general rule shoots that are flowering do not make good cutting material, particularly for woody plants. It seems that the physiological state of the tissue of flowering material is much less conducive to adventitious root formation than non-flowering material. It should be noted, though, that there are plenty of cases of plants that will root quite happily even when they are covered in flowers. Numerous herbaceous species such as impatiens can be rooted in a matter of days. While this is possible it is often not ideal, especially as far as commercial production goes, since flower buds developing on the cutting will divert energy away from vegetative growth and normally we are looking to build a strong vegetative framework before flowering occurs. This is especially so with plants that flower terminally, in other words, vegetative growth of the shoot ceases altogether before flowering occurs. For such species, for example chrysanthemums and poinsettias, it is absolutely critical that cuttings are not in the flowering stage.

Chrysanthemums and poinsettias have become extremely important ornamental crops, mainly because their flowering response can be easily and reproducibly manipulated by controlling the daylength they are held under. In both cases, flowering occurs in response to shortening of daylength (or to be more accurate, increasing nightlength) so that daylengths of 12 hours or more will guarantee that stock plants remain in a vegetative state. This can be achieved by mounting lights—either normal incandescent or cool white fluorescent lights—three metres above the stock plants with intervals between lights of two metres. They are then turned on during the night for the period required to push the daylength above the critical level. Usually this is achieved by the use of automatic timers and a four-hour period of illumination is programmed for the middle of the night (although other programmes will work equally well). Once cuttings are struck, they are initially grown under extended daylengths until they reach the desired height. The lights are then turned off and, depending on the time of year, it may be necessary to shorten the daylength with 'blackout curtains' to give the plants the critical daylength for flowering. Each cultivar has its own **response time**, this being the number of weeks it will take to flower after the plant is subjected to short day conditions.

Seed orchards

There are many important groups of plants that are routinely propagated by seed. Vegetables, cereals and trees are perhaps the most prominent. The source of the seed is a vital consideration, particularly for tree species which are likely to be growing for many decades. A knowledge of the seed's genetic makeup allows the propagator to predict the potential of the plants and ensure that the grower gets what they want. Production of seed of annuals such as vegetables and flowering plants is undertaken by specialist seed companies, especially when F1 hybrid seed is being offered. Such seed requires the input of plant breeders (see section in Chapter 3 on F1 hybrid seed). Where non-F1 hybrid vegetable and flower seed is involved, it is often possible to save seed from such plants and have them remain true to type (see section in Chapter 3 on Seed Savers Network).

Seed sources for tree and shrub species present an interesting challenge for plant propagators. For many species, collection of seed is a relatively easy task. For example, eucalypts produce woody seed capsules that remain indefinitely on the tree and provide a ready source of seed. However, as was discussed in Chapter 3, the seed collector must carefully consider the situation of the parent tree—is it true to type and are there any closely related species nearby with which it may have hybridised? Because these are often very difficult questions to answer, the logical solution is to collect seed from trees specially set aside for the purpose of seed production. For woody species being propagated from seed, it is often extremely useful, and sometimes essential, to know where the seed was collected in the wild, in other words, its original geographic source—this is known as its **provenance**. Many woody plant species have a very wide geographic spread and this results in the formation of **ecotypes.** These are genetically distinct races that form in response to differences in climate and soil type which result from the varying latitude, longitude and altitude that these ecotypes grow in. Consider for instance the river red gum, *Eucalyptus camaldulensis*, which grows in every mainland state of Australia, particularly along watercourses, but also on low mountain slopes such as in the Mt Lofty Ranges near Adelaide. The trees which result from seed collection in the different provenances vary in all sorts of important characteristics such as frost tolerance, growth habit and growth rate. Most interesting, perhaps, is the variation in salt tolerance. Provenances such as Lake Albacutya in Victoria have yielded trees that are able to withstand extreme salt concentrations and these have proved to be vital in the reclamation and rehabilitation of saline soils in affected farmlands around the planet.

Another example is the ribbon gum, *Eucalyptus viminalis,* a species which occupies an extraordinarily wide range of ecological niches. It can be found as a dwarf five metre high tree in coastal heathland or a forest giant of 40 metres in well-watered alluvial soils in the valleys created by the Great Dividing Range. In addition, there is a full range of intermediate types in the habitats between those two extremes. The choice of seed stock can be tailored to the end purpose to which the trees will be put.

Seed provenance information will be available from reputable seed companies and it is worthwhile researching such information to establish which provenance will be most suited to the task at hand. Another interesting situation has been created by the increasing focus on **bush regeneration** in Australia. For those interested in maintaining the genetic diversity of their local bushland, it is vital that plants are regenerated from **indigenous seed collections**, i.e. seed is collected in areas that bear as close an association as possible to the area to be regenerated.

In other situations, such as forestry where high yield is the most important consideration, seed is collected from parent trees that are known to produce genetically superior offspring. This is usually established by **progeny testing**, a process that involves growing out populations of seedlings from various parent trees and assessing which are superior. These superior parent trees are then marked and, if possible, they are propagated vegetatively. In addition, a planting is established in an isolated area, with several different clones being used to enable cross pollination between the superior trees, giving better seed set and lowering the chances of inbreeding which can cause a loss in vigour. Various cultural practices are employed to try and make the trees flower and therefore seed as soon as possible (see the example below on eucalyptus seed orchards).

Eucalyptus seed orchards

Eucalypts are arguably the most widely planted genus of trees worldwide, being planted in over 90 countries and in every continent for commercial purposes. This has led to a demand for millions of eucalypt seedlings every year. There is ever-increasing interest in genetically improved seed and the establishment of seed orchards to supply it. To this end, CSIRO scientists Michael Moncur and Peter Burgess have developed techniques to enhance the efficiency of eucalypt seed orchards. See Eucalypt Domestication and Breeding in Further Reading.

Such measures include shortening the juvenile period (during which plants will not flower) by grafting shoots of selected eucalypts on to older root-stocks. When the grafted shoots reach a convenient height for harvest, they are treated with **paclobutrazol**, a plant growth regulator which alters the hormonal balance in the plant, causing vegetative growth to slow, which in turn stimulates flowering and subsequent seeding. The time to reach flow-ering was reduced in *E. globulus* from five to seven years to three years. Plants were also *espaliered*, that is, they were trained onto a trellis to further aid the dwarfing treatment that brings earlier seed production. The result was some rather weird looking eucalypts that were, nonetheless, hundreds of times more productive when it came to seed production.

CHAPTER **12**

Environmental Control

Most techniques of plant propagation will be greatly enhanced by some degree of environmental control and there are numerous ways of achieving this. At a backyard level it is possible to improvise in all sorts of ways (see Environmental Control in the Home Garden later in this chapter) to keep costs down. Most plants for your garden can be readily propagated with minimal facilities. On the other hand, if it is a commercial exercise, the efficiency of the operation will be considerably improved by judicious investment in appropriate environmental controls. The decision about what sort of structure and equipment to use will be decided by the scale of the operation and the funds available. Great advances in technology have been made in this area in the past couple of decades, with ever more sophisticated computer-controlled equipment becoming available.

It should be said that there is a lot of propagation that can be done with no environmental control—things like aerial layering of outdoor shrubs, direct sowing of seed and sticking hardwood cuttings directly into unprotected garden beds. One should never underestimate the resilience of plants and their ability to survive, particularly at the home garden level where 100 per cent success is often not a crucial objective—in other words, if only a few cuttings strike out of a batch, that is usually enough.

Structures for Plant Propagation

The detail of technology and construction of the various greenhouses is a specialist topic and beyond the scope of this book. Books such as Keith Garzoli's *Greenhouses* should be consulted for further reading on this topic.

Glasshouses and greenhouses

Glass was the traditional material used for propagation in decades gone by. It has increasingly fallen out of favour due to its cost and breakability. Various materials such as horticultural plastics (plastics that are reinforced to withstand ultraviolet radiation), fibreglass and polycarbonate plastic have become increasingly popular for reasons of cost in the case of the first two, and durability in the latter. These materials can be used to cover all sorts of structures, from igloos to lean-to or freestanding gable-roof constructions. Propagation activities requiring a high level of environmental control, such as leaf and softwood cuttings, are carried out in these structures.

Cold frames

These are like miniature greenhouses, often constructed as lean-to structures against the walls of buildings or greenhouses. They are usually 50–70 centimetres in height and covered with a tight fitting lid of either glass or plastic.They are generally unheated, although it is a simple matter to include bottom heated beds as well, to enable faster production. Cold frames provide an excellent low-cost method of creating propagating space. Cold frames are useful for propagation methods that do not require a high degree of environmental control, such as hardwood cuttings, seedling production and division.

Shadehouses

These are very simple structures that are usually freestanding and are covered in a material designed to allow the passage of air and water. Coverings such as woven synthetic fabrics (shadecloth) or wooden slats are used. The degree of shade can be varied by selecting different grades of shadecloth, and the choice will depend on the purpose of the shadehouse. Generally they are used to **'harden off'** propagated plants from more intensive greenhouse environments. In effect, shadehouses provide an environmental bridge to gradually acclimatise plants to uncontrolled conditions. In addition, shadehouses can be used as the initial location for many propagation procedures such as seed raising, hardwood cuttings and root cuttings.

Methods of Environmental Control

The various environmental factors that can be controlled include humidity, temperature of the atmosphere and the medium, light and carbon dioxide.

Clockwise from bottom left: A very simple form of greenhouse using cut down drink bottles; Simple portable timber cold frames make for a versatile method of environmental control; Plastic tubing carries hot water to provide bottom heat for propagation, capillary matting is placed on top of the plastic tubing; Australian Plant Society member Ross Doig shows off a simple home propagator created from a cut-down polystyrene fruit box and a plastic lid.

Let us look at some of the strategies for creating the ideal propagation environment.

Humidity

- **Humidity tents:** A plastic tent is erected over the propagation bench to create a very highly controlled micro-climate inside a greenhouse or shadehouse. They are particularly useful in structures where there is very little control, such as shadehouses. If bottom heating is provided on the bench inside the humidity tent, temperature can also be easily controlled. The humidity tent should be capable of being opened and closed easily to enable the plant material to be hardened off and moved around with a minimum of fuss. Propagators in the nineteenth century used a technique called 'syringing' where a hand mister was used on a regular basis to increase humidity inside a humidity tent. While this is feasible where labour is readily available, it does not sit well with modern business where labour must be reduced at all costs. The answer is to provide misting or fogging nozzles (see above) which can be automatically regulated. Another problem with humidity tents is that the temperature inside tends to increase rapidly on a sunny day, and shading is required

Left: Misting nozzles inside a humidity tent. Right: A misting nozzle.

to stop the plants from 'cooking'. Whilst shading is quite feasible, it means reducing the light levels, thereby reducing photosynthesis in the propagules and forcing them to draw on their own food reserves to survive. Again, misting or fogging can also be used as a means of lowering the temperature.

- **Misting:** This refers to the process of spraying a mist of fine water droplets into the atmosphere of the propagation area. When the technique was first developed in the 1940s it proved to be a major breakthrough, particularly for the production of softwood cuttings. Misting is not done continuously, however, as this would result in too much water being applied, causing all sorts of disease problems. To avoid such problems, **intermittent mist systems** are used so that the misters only come on when humidity drops below a certain predetermined level. This level is determined by the type of plant, the type of wood being used and the ambient temperature and humidity.

An important point with misting systems is that a film of water is deposited on the leaf surface by the mist and this has the effect of lowering the temperature of the leaf, thereby greatly decreasing transpiration (water loss) from the leaf. This in turn prevents the leaf from wilting. This regular reduction in temperature allows us to maintain much higher light levels in the propagation environment, which means that levels of photosynthesis are increased which in turn means that the cutting becomes self-sufficient much quicker. The result is that roots form faster and the turn-around time for a batch of cuttings is decreased. In addition, softwood cuttings can be taken while they are still very soft—early in the growing season, when they are at their best as far as root formation is concerned. In my experience the optimum interval between mistings allows the film of water on the leaf to evaporate before the next burst of mist replaces it.

The process has been refined over the years to the point where it can be reliably automated using various devices which monitor the propagation environment 24 hours a day. When environmental conditions (humidity is normally the factor used, but temperature or light levels can be used in conjunction with humidity) reach a certain level determined by the propagator, a switch (usually a solenoid device) is triggered to turn the misters on until the humidity rises above the desired level. There are numerous devices for controlling these systems and advice should be sought from a local propagator as to the best system available in a particular area. Reliability is perhaps the most important issue with such systems.

■ **Fogging:** This refers to a system where extremely fine droplets of water are injected into the propagation area to create a 'fog'. The major practical difference between fogging and misting is that the droplet size of the 'fog' is so small that the droplets remain suspended in the air, while mist droplets fall rapidly to the ground under the force of gravity. Thus, there is not the tendency for the leaf to be coated in a film of water as with misting. This tends to lead to a lessening in leaf diseases as the fungal and bacterial organisms that cause them often germinate much better on a leaf surface coated with water. Fogging systems tend to be more expensive to install as it is somewhat harder to generate the very fine droplets for fog than the larger droplets for mist. For small-scale propagation, a small plug-in vaporiser (of the sort used for treating respiratory complaints) is a cheap and easy substitute for a commercial system. It is possible to link such a machine to a control system and automate the process as well, or alternatively set the machine up in a humidity tent of reasonable size and turn the machine on and off manually as required to get the humidity up to the desired levels. Such a system will obviously require much more intensive supervision by the propagator.

Temperature

■ **Heating systems:** The temperature of the propagation environment can be altered in two different ways. **Bottom heating** refers to any system which supplies heat to the base of the propagule. Heating the propagation medium in this way tends to greatly increase root growth. It is also a much more efficient way of heating the general propagation environment, particularly where some means of trapping the air immediately above the bench can be employed. Various systems are available and the choice will depend on factors such as cost and availability. In the past, insulated electrical cables have been embedded in a medium such as fine sand with the heat having to permeate up through the sand. A more recent and perhaps more effective innovation is the use of moulded plastic mats that contain a network of fine tubes which allow hot water to circulate. The propagation containers are placed directly onto the mats. In my experience this provides a far more efficient and direct way of supplying bottom heat. **Aerial heating** is a common feature of most propagation houses and can be provided in many different ways, the choice often being governed by the cost and availability of fuels for the multitude of systems available. Perhaps the key to efficient aerial heating is the provision of thermal screens above the plants (see below).

■ **Cooling systems:** This is often an extremely important issue in the scorching summers encountered in many parts of Australia. A degree of cooling can be achieved through the use of **passive ventilation** by having vents in the sides and roof of the house which can be opened either manually or automatically, by linking them to a thermostat. If one remembers the principle that hot air rises, it is a fairly simple matter to place vents in the ceiling. It is also important to have side vents as well so that as the air evacuates through the roof vents, fresh air can be drawn into the bottom of the house through the side vents. Benches to be used for delicate propagation work such as softwood cuttings should not be placed right next to the vents, however. In many cases passive ventilation will not be sufficient to provide the degree of cooling necessary, and some form of **active ventilation** is required. **Evaporative cooling** is a commonly used system which utilises a fan to suck air through a moistened pad, causing it to cool before it goes into the greenhouse. **Exhaust fans** can be used in conjunction with vents to simply speed up the movement of air through the house, allowing for fresh, cooler air to be brought in. Other more powerful refrigeration systems are available but they are expensive, and it is best to consult an expert in this field before making a decision.

■ **Thermal screens:** Various materials can be used to provide a screen that can be drawn across the house to provide cooling in summer and heat retention in winter. A popular option at present are the so-called L.S. screens (named for their inventor Ludwig Svensson), which are plastic screens with strips of aluminium embedded in them. Such a system allows whatever degree of shading is required in summer (through different grades of material), while in winter the screen can be used to stop heat escaping by drawing it across at night or on cold days. A thermal screen also reduces the volume of air above the crop to be heated, thereby reducing heating costs.

Light
There are two aspects of lighting in the propagation environment—providing supplementary light for photosynthesis, and control of daylength.

- **Supplementary photosynthetic lighting:** In the Australian environment, light for photosynthesis is usually plentiful. However, in cases where light levels are very low, particularly in winter, it is possible to use supplementary lighting to boost growth. There are various options for delivering the extra light. In the unlikely event that supplementary lighting is required, it is best to seek expert advice on the topic as it is a very specialized area of technology which is constantly changing.

- **Daylength control**: Several important ornamental plants flower in response to changing daylength. Examples include Geraldton wax (*Chamelaucium uncinatum*), chrysanthemum (*Dendranthema* spp.) and poinsettia (*Euphorbia pulcherrima*). These species are induced to flower by short-day treatments which are provided by using blackout curtains during crop production. The crucial aspect for propagation, however, is to prevent flower initiation by providing long day conditions so that the struck cuttings are in a vegetative state when the grower receives them. They are then grown on in long day conditions until sufficient vegetative growth has occurred to provide the framework for the finished flowering product. Suitable long day conditions for maintaining vegetative growth can be provided by mounting either normal cool white fluorescent or incandescent lighting no more than a couple of metres above the plants with a couple of metres between light fittings along the rows of plants. The simplest system in my experience is then to turn the lights on in the middle of the night for a four hour period. This can be achieved easily by using a timing switch that can be set to allow the lights to be turned on and off automatically.

Carbon Dioxide

- **Carbon dioxide (CO_2) injection:** Plants use CO_2 as part of the process of photosynthesis and its supply can become a limiting factor in poorly ventilated greenhouses. In a reasonably well-ventilated greenhouse, CO_2 enters from the external atmosphere and replaces that being used up by the plants inside. Attention to ventilation of the greenhouse will ensure that the supply of CO_2 is adequate, as well as taking care of other problems such as minimising fungal leaf diseases. If for some reason ventilation is an insurmountable problem, cylinders of CO_2 can be used to inject extra CO_2 into the greenhouse atmosphere. Once again, it is best to seek expert advice on the best way to implement this operation.

Environmental Control in the Home Garden

Plant propagation at home is very different from the commercial situation in which growers must always strive for the highest success rates possible. For the home gardener high success rates are obviously desirable, but usually many more plants will be produced than can ever be utilised. What this means is that home gardeners can get away with techniques which are much less stringent than commercial propagators. In the remainder of this chapter, I would like to share some of the techniques which can be applied successfully on a small scale.

Create your own greenhouse from recycled materials

A miniature greenhouse can be created by recycling various materials from around the house. Clear plastic bottles can be used by cutting off the base and simply placing the top of the bottle over your cuttings, making sure to press it into the soil so it is firmly anchored over the plants. Place your mini greenhouse in a sheltered position out of direct sunlight, or if direct sunlight is unavoidable, simply wrap a layer of shadecloth around the bottle.

Another great alternative for larger numbers of cuttings or seedlings is to take a polystyrene fruit box and punch 10 to 15 holes in the base. The box can either be filled directly with propagation medium, or individual pots placed in the box. The top of the box is covered with one of the following—plastic, a sheet of glass, shadecloth or even moistened newspaper—depending on what is being propagated and at what time of year.

Propagation structures for the home garden

If you wish to go a little bit more 'high tech', there are a number of do-it-yourself greenhouse kits available through the various gardening magazines. The main thing I would suggest you look out for in these is that the structure has adequate provision for ventilation. Most sorts of greenhouses are good at trapping heat, which is obviously the name of the game in winter. Where some greenhouses fall down, particularly in warmer climates, is in the warmer months of the year when getting rid of heat becomes the most important issue. A good greenhouse will have retractable vents both in the roof and in the walls. Since hot air rises, roof vents are critical to efficiently removing heat. If there are wall vents open as well, the hot air moving out from the roof will establish a flow, drawing in cooler air through the wall vents. Not only does the ventilation allow for cooling, but the fresh air also replenishes the supply of carbon dioxide for photosynthesis, and air movement tends to stop the development of debilitating fungal leaf diseases.

Another advanced option for a propagation structure is a bottom heated tray with a clear, fully enclosed lid. These types of structures, which are once again available through gardening magazines, have heating elements embedded in the base of the tray which are electrically powered and simply plug in to a normal power socket. A removable clear plastic lid fits neatly on top to enclose the tray and maintain humidity. The option of bottom heating can be used to improve the speed of rooting of cuttings (particularly difficult-to-strike ones) and germination of seedlings.

Summary of Environmental Control

Vast amounts of money can be spent on environmental control systems to achieve an absolutely perfect propagation environment. It is very important that consideration be given to achieving a balance that enables cost-effective propagation. In other words, the expense of creating perfect conditions may not be justified economically, and it may be better to accept a slightly lesser propagation result in order to ensure profitability.

It is also vital to not become complacent when using automatic controllers for the various pieces of equipment for environmental control. No automatic system is infallible, and they are only as good as the person programming them. In my experience, it is essential to check the plant material several times a day if it is at a sensitive stage, such as newly prepared softwood cuttings. There can be no substitute for the vigilance and intuition of the experienced propagator.

CHAPTER 13

Other Issues in Plant Propagation

Pests and Diseases, Hygiene and Sanitation, Media and Hormones

Consider the situation that is created in the average plant propagation area. For many propagation methods, greenhouses are maintained under warm, humid conditions that are not only ideal for the development of plants but also for many types of organisms that are pathogenic (disease-causing) to those plants. In addition, we also have very high planting densities which provide a veritable feast for any pests or diseases that are introduced to the area. The traditional approach to these problems in recent decades has been to rely heavily on chemicals as a preventative treatment, with fungicides and pesticides being used routinely whether or not there is any sign of pests or diseases.

In recent years it has become increasingly apparent that disease-causing organisms are often able to evolve new genetic strains that are resistant to the chemical treatments that have controlled them in the past. In fact, the faster we pour the chemicals on, generally the quicker will be the evolution of a resistant strain, since we are increasing the selection pressure. Increasingly, the idea of integrated pest management is being applied to pest and disease control (for further detail refer to Chapter 11). This concept involves looking at every possible way of minimising damage to the plants by the organism concerned. In such a strategy chemicals tend to be looked on as a last resort after all other methods have been exhausted. To make such an approach fully effective, we need to study the problem organism in its entirety in order to understand the life cycle. In this way, we can understand how each problem organism spreads through the propagation area and hence take steps to prevent this happening. Let us now look in turn at the most common problem organisms.

Pests and Diseases—Fungi

Damping off, seed rot, root rot

Damping off is a general term used to describe the death of seeds, seedlings, tissue culture plantlets or cuttings and it can potentially affect virtually every species of plant grown in the nursery. The term damping off is used because the plant material often takes on a slimy, watery texture when it rots away. A variety of fungi have been found to cause damping off, and this makes chemical control a difficult proposition, as specific products will be required depending on the exact identity of the organism causing the problem. The main organisms involved are *Pythium* species, *Phytophthora* species (both belonging to the Phycomycete or water mould group of fungi), *Rhizoctonia* species and *Botrytis* species (both belonging to the Ascomycete or imperfect group of fungi). Chemicals effective against the Phycomycete group are generally not effective against the Ascomycete group, and vice versa. Since it is normally very difficult or impossible to identify which type of fungus is involved, controlling the problem becomes rather difficult. If the problem will result in large economic losses it is best to get the organism identified by a plant pathologist in order to work out the best method of attack, particularly if the losses become large enough to make chemical control necessary. In the case of damping off, prevention through good hygiene becomes even more important than normal, given the difficulty in controlling it once it becomes established.

- **Symptoms of damping off:** Symptoms occur both before and after the plant emerges from the growing medium. In **pre-emergence damping off** the seeds rot off before germinating or seedlings rot before emerging above the growing medium. In **post-emergence damping off**, as the name suggests, rotting occurs after emergence of the seedling and can manifest as stem rot, wire stem, top damping off or basal rot of cuttings. **Stem rot**—the stem rots at ground level and the seedling falls over. This is usually caused by *Phytophthora*, *Pythium* or *Rhizoctonia*. **Wire stem**— as for stem rot, but the seedling remains standing. This particularly affects seedlings where the stem is reasonably strong, for example, eucalypts. The seedling may die or be considerably weakened causing problems weeks or months later, particularly under conditions of water stress. It is usually caused by *Rhizoctonia*. **Top damping off**—the fungus spreads through the leaves or stems above ground and rots the plant from the top down to the base, often leaving the root system intact. It is particularly serious in conditions of high humidity, such as with intermittent mist or fogging systems. It is often a serious problem with soft tip cuttings and seedlings which have not been transplanted quickly enough and become leggy. Usually caused by *Phytophthora, Pythium* or *Botrytis*. **Basal rot of cuttings** —fungi enter through wounds at the base of the cutting where leaves have been removed or where the stem has been cut.

■ **Control of damping off:** The ubiquitous nature of the fungi that cause this problem means that it is very difficult to control. The spores can be spread very easily by water splash and water flow every time plants are irrigated. It is therefore very important to try to prevent the transfer of water from container to container by placing them on raised benches. Hygiene is critically important, especially when you are dealing with very soft plant material such as seedlings or tissue cultured plantlets. New

The devastating results of damping off in seedlings.

containers, or at least ones that have been thoroughly cleaned are recommended, as well as a medium that is pasteurised or is made of sterile ingredients such as vermiculite or perlite. Removal of diseased material as soon as it appears is highly desirable. The use of fungicides such as Previcur® and Fongarid® can be helpful. It is important, however, to identify the organism involved before investing too much money in fungicides. These fungicides are normally used as drenches, applied by means of watering cans or some other suitable method. Take care to follow all precautions advised by the manufacturer.

Botrytis cinerea

This is commonly known as grey mould and is an enormous problem in greenhouses generally and propagation houses in particular. It is a disease that is favoured by high humidity, warm temperatures and still air, exactly the type of conditions that we strive to create on an intensive propagation bench. Perhaps because it is so common and widespread, it has started to develop resistance to many of the fungicides used to control it. In this situation, the grower has very little option but to return to the drawing board by either growing species that are resistant to the fungus or trying to alter the environmental conditions so they are less suited to the fungus. Ensuring good air flow around plants is crucial, so practices such as lowering planting densities and using fans to keep air circulating within the greenhouse will add up to lower botrytis levels. Another thing that growers can do is to maintain very high levels of hygiene and, in particular, remove infected leaves or whole plants as soon as any sign of botrytis appears. Use of fungicides should be the last option, as constant routine use will lead more rapidly to a resistant strain of fungus.

Fusarium oxysporum

This fungus causes vascular wilts in a wide range of species, both exotic and Australian. It is a major problem in crops such as carnation. Because it affects the vascular (sap and water conducting) tissue inside the plant, it is extremely difficult to control. Obviously it is a disastrous state of affairs if a disease like this gets loose in propagation stock. Any affected material should be immediately discarded. The use of disease-indexed mother stock for the initial plant material is an excellent way of guarding against fusarium in a commercial situation. The usual practices of good hygiene are also critical.

Other Pests and Diseases

Bacteria

Certain plant pathogenic bacteria can cause havoc in propagation areas due to their preference for moist, humid conditions. The genus *Erwinia* is responsible for soft rot diseases which have similar symptoms to damping off, in that the plant tissue tends to collapse in a watery, slimy, stinking mess. Similar hygiene measures as for damping off diseases need to be taken. Copper-based sprays such as copper oxychloride and Bordeaux mixture are about the only effective chemical measures that can be taken.

Viruses

These are one of the most difficult of all propagation problems to deal with. Viruses are extremely simple organisms which can only multiply when they are inside the cells of their host organism. The great problem is that once they do get inside those cells, it is extremely difficult to get rid of them. In fact, for the worst viruses the only way to kill them is to kill the host—a fairly drastic solution in anyone's language! The symptoms of viral diseases are sometimes difficult to recognise, but they include yellowing and/or streaking of the leaves and stunting and poor vigour of the plants generally. There are many types of viruses and they tend to be specific to particular types of plants. There are no chemical controls for viruses.

The use of mother stock that has been tested (or indexed) to ensure that it is virus free is the starting point for commercial plant propagators. Indexing programmes exist for some of the more important food and ornamental crops. Such programmes must be run by qualified plant pathologists and it is generally worth contacting state departments of agriculture to see what programmes are being run in different regions. Once virus-free mother stock is obtained, it is essential to keep it that way. The trick to controlling the spread of viruses lies in understanding how they spread—by the transfer of plant sap from the vascular system of an infected plant to an uninfected one. Viruses can be transferred by a variety of sap sucking insect pests such as aphids, thrips, mealy bugs and leaf hoppers or by tools such as secateurs and knives. Quarantining stock plants in greenhouses protected by insect-proof netting and regular sterilisation of propagation tools are the keys to stopping the spread of viral diseases.

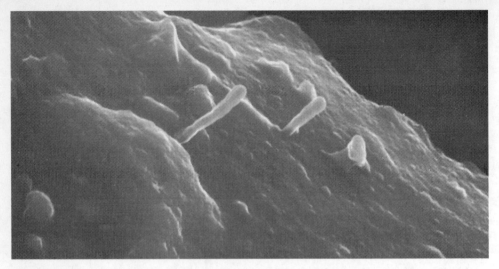

Fungal spores germinating on a sand particle. Magnified 7000 times.

Sciarid fly

The sciarid fly (also known as fungus gnat) can be quite an insidious pest, particularly in intensive propagation facilities. The adults are reminiscent of fruit flies and they will often be spotted crawling on the surface of propagation media. They lay their eggs in the medium and when these hatch the voracious microscopic larvae are unleashed. The larvae are barely visible to the naked eye and can be identified by their black heads and opaque bodies. The larvae feed on organic matter, both living and dead, and they will feed on a wide range of plant species. The larvae will attack roots of seedlings and cuttings and even the stem base of cuttings, bulbs and corms. The larvae can also bore their way inside the stems of cuttings such as chrysanthemums and poinsettias and eventually cause them to collapse completely. They pose a nasty threat because often they have done a great deal of damage before the propagator realises what is causing it, since all the damage is happening below the surface of the medium. An extremely wide range of crops is affected by sciarid fly larvae, and it is essential for the commercial plant propagator to be familiar with this pest. A hand lens is necessary to make a positive diagnosis.

Control of this pest is rather difficult as the larvae can burrow inside the stems of cuttings and this makes it difficult to contact them with chemical controls. (Consult your state department of agriculture for a list of recommended registered chemicals.) An exciting recent development has been the discovery and development of a beneficial nematode that is capable of controlling this pest. It is available commercially (see details in Appendix 3) and is harmful only to insects—in other words it is totally safe to humans and other animals. Drip irrigation or a watering can is used to drench the plants with water in which the nematodes are suspended.

Sap sucking pests

This category includes a wide variety of insects such as aphids, thrips, whiteflies, scale insects and mealy bugs. Using stock plants that are infected with these pests is perhaps the most common way of introducing them. Appropriate stock plant management is therefore a critical part of the control strategy for this group of pests. Pests such as thrips, whiteflies and aphids are able to fly into the propagation house, so if possible outside sources of infestation should be monitored closely and controlled.

Weeds

These are a problem where there is poor hygiene in and around the propagation house or if contaminated media is used. Weeds are easily dealt with by appropriate hygiene and sanitation measures as listed below.

Hygiene and Sanitation

One of the best ways of minimising the damage from pests and diseases is to exclude them in the first place by sound hygiene practices. It is important to realise that different pests and diseases are spread in different ways. Each organism therefore requires different measures and these are listed above for the relevant pest or disease.

Think of hygiene and sanitation in terms of human health. We are taught from an early age to automatically wash hands after going to the toilet or wiping down the kitchen bench—such practices become second nature as we know that failure to follow them can result in the spread of human pathogens. In propagation areas fungi, bacteria and weed seeds are commonly spread by infected potting mix ingredients, infected leaves, clothes, dust, workboots and machinery. We therefore need to regularly monitor the cleanliness of our propagation areas and keep them as clean and tidy as we would our kitchens. Regularly dispose of plant debris, sterilise pots that are being recycled, swab down benches between operations and generally be as vigilant as possible. See Appendix 3 for details of sterilants and other treatments that can be safely used in the propagation area.

Stopping the spread of viruses presents a different challenge, as we must stop the transfer of sap from plant to plant by regularly sterilising our cutting tools in situations where viruses are likely to be present. Tools can be dipped in sterilant or boiling water, or it may even be worthwhile investing in secateurs that have been equipped with a special device that squirts a small amount of sterilant onto the blade after each cut. Such secateurs are made by companies such as Felco and may be difficult to obtain in Australia, but it may be well worth the trouble for virus-prone plants such as orchids. Exclusion of sap sucking insects such as aphids, whitefly, thrips and leaf hoppers is also vital to preventing viral infections. For very valuable propagation stock, plants can be grown in insect-proof greenhouses under strict quarantine conditions so that no passing 'sap-suckers' can accidentally infect your elite plants.

Potting mixes are another major factor to be considered in excluding pests and diseases from the propagation area. There are many options for providing the basic ingredients for propagation mixes and these should be selected so as to minimise the chances of having a medium that is already contaminated with pathogens. The next section provides a complete guide to this subject.

Methods of hygiene and sanitation

Bleach solutions. A common and readily available sterilant is household bleach (sodium hypochlorite), a substance used to keep bathrooms free of germs. A solution that contains 1 per cent available chlorine is normally used for swabbing down table tops and similar surfaces. Most laundry and household bleach products contain around 4 per cent available chlorine so a 1 part bleach to 3 parts water solution will give the required strength. It should be said that while bleach is an effective sterilant, it is also a very corrosive substance that will cause rusting of metal and bleaching of clothes. Inhaling bleach for lengthy periods of time can also cause irritation of respiratory passages. For these reasons, other sterilants should also be considered, depending on the situation. Quaternary ammonium compounds are also commonly used as household products, or for more powerful agents hospital grade sterilants such as Biogram® could also be used at the recommended rate. These latter sterilants are particularly good for use on secateurs and propagation knives where bleach solutions will cause corrosion.

Pasteurisation of potting mixes is also a key part of keeping the propagation area free of pests and diseases. Pasteurisation involves treating media with aerated steam such that the whole body of the medium heats up to 60 degrees Celsius for at least 30 minutes. This process requires rather specialised equipment such as a boiler and special trolleys that allow the medium to be enclosed and treated with the steam for extended periods of time. It is worth asking with large potting mix manufacturers about their capacity to pasteurise, as many of them will be able to provide you with this service.

Integrated Pest and Disease Management in the Propagation House

The modern approach to pests and diseases is to try to minimise the use of toxic chemicals by applying every possible means of reducing pest and disease populations. Good quarantine, hygiene and sanitation procedures will greatly assist in reducing populations in the first instance. Suitable spacings of plants to increase air circulation will help to reduce fungal diseases. The use of pasteurised potting mixes will give propagules a head start. Various beneficial organisms are now available to help reduce problems both in the propagation house and in mother stock plantings used for cuttings (see chrysanthemum example in Chapter 11, Stock Plant Management).

Media for Plant Propagation

An enormous array of possibilities exists when it comes to the topic of propagation media. In the home garden it is certainly possible to improvise quite a lot, and for some methods of propagation such as layering, division and hardwood cuttings, it is feasible to use straight garden soil as your medium, provided it is friable and has a reasonably good crumb structure. However, for best results and particularly in commercial situations, it is better to construct mixes for particular propagation purposes.

Whatever raw materials are selected for your propagation media, they must be capable of fitting a certain set of criteria. The medium must be cost-effective, readily available and uniform in quality. It must be free of pests, weeds and most importantly, diseases. It must be able to retain sufficient moisture so that watering does not have to be too frequent yet still be well-drained and most importantly for cuttings, well-aerated. It must be capable of providing sufficient support for the propagules and should not be saline or contain toxic substances.

It must also be appreciated that different propagation methods may require different media in order to get optimum results. In other words the medium used for seed raising is quite different to that used for cuttings. In the home garden it is possible to get away with using a single medium that gives reasonable results for all propagation methods, but for the serious propagator it is certainly worth the trouble of modifying your mix for specific purposes. Let us look now at some of the common ingredients of propagation mixes and their properties.

- **Sand:** Perhaps the most common ingredient used, it consists of rock fragments varying in size from 0.02–2.0 millimetres. Given this rather large range of particle size, there are numerous grades of sand available. Finer grades are used in seed raising mixes, where the smaller particles help to retain a little more water in the mix. Coarser grades are useful in mixes for cuttings, where the larger particles give much higher levels of aeration. Sharp sand (i.e. sand with very angular edges) is preferred for cutting mixes and it is usually washed to get rid of finer particles and in particular the small amounts of clay and silt that are often present in the raw material. Sand is excellent for providing mixes with ballast (weight) as many other ingredients such as peat and perlite are extremely light and, on their own, they may not give the propagules enough support. In most cases sands do not provide any nutrients and do not have the capacity to store either nutrients or water. Sand is also extremely stable in both its physical and chemical properties. It can be used to provide the 'backbone' of the medium.
- **Peats and peatmosses:** These materials are the remains of aquatic, marsh, bog or swamp vegetation that has partially decomposed under waterlogged conditions. The partial decomposition process removes many of the sugars and nutrients, but the basic cellular structure of the plant remains and most of its humus. Thus peatmoss is basically a collection of miniature, hollow stems that act like sponges and absorb large amounts of water relative to their volume. In addition, their organic base means that they are able to store any nutrients that are applied to the potting mix. Peatmoss is extremely variable, however, as the type of plant that has formed it will have a great effect on its properties. Sphagnum

peat, for instance, is derived from herbaceous acid bog plants of the genus *Sphagnum*, and its unique structure makes it the most open of all peats, giving it excellent aeration and high water holding capacity—it makes an excellent medium for cuttings on its own. At the other extreme are peats derived from all sorts of different bog plants that have much lower air and water holding capacities and are therefore not as useful for propagation media. Peat that is good for propagation will be rather fluffy in nature. Another problem with peat is its acidity (pH 3.5–4.5), which makes the addition of lime essential in peat-based mixes. Peats also tend to shrink when they dry out and become difficult to rewet, a problem that can be overcome by the use of wetting agents. It should also be pointed out that the world's reserves of peat are being depleted rather rapidly and perhaps it is time for horticulturists to move towards other products that can be substituted quite successfully for peat.

- **Coir or coconut fibre:** This material has emerged in recent years as a logical successor to peat for potting mixes and other uses. It is a byproduct of the processing of coconuts and is therefore a renewable resource. If properly processed, it has properties very similar to peat and in my experience can be used very successfully in propagation mixes in the same proportions as peat. A word of caution, however, as the quality of some of the products on the market is variable, depending on the source of the fibre. Perhaps the best policy is to purchase a product manufactured by one of the larger reputable potting mix manufacturers.

- **Composted pine bark:** This material is now a standard ingredient of many potting mixes and it has been used quite successfully in propagation mixes. One of the advantages of pine bark is that it can be crushed and screened to give particles of a known size range, with 0.5 to 2.0 millimetre particles being suitable for propagation mixes. The material is light, reasonably stable and well aerated due to coarse particle size, but is still able to hold moderate amounts of water. It is on the acidic side, but not as much as peat. It does not store nutrients as well as peat.

- **Perlite:** This interesting material is derived from a natural volcanic glass mineral that is found in various deposits around the world. When heated to very high temperature (1000–1200 degrees Celsius), it expands dramatically to form fluffy white granules that are white and very porous in nature. It has a neutral pH (7) and, being based on silica, it does not supply or store nutrients to any great extent. It can be purchased in various particle sizes to suit different media requirements and an enormous advantage is that it is sterile after its high temperature processing. It can therefore be relied upon to be disease-free when it comes out of its bag. Its porous structure also means that it can store significant quantities of available water. Its major drawback is its relatively high cost, but where high value plants such as micropropagated plantlets are being raised perlite may be a cost-effective choice, given its numerous advantages. As well as being used in mixtures with other ingredients it can also be used alone as a medium for cutting production. In this case, however, the propagator must bear in mind that it does not supply or store any nutrients. Another point to note is that perlite generates a dust that can be very irritating to those with respiratory conditions such as asthma—use a dust mask or respirator when pouring perlite out of its bag.

- **Vermiculite:** This is a flaky mica-like mineral that occurs naturally. Like perlite it is heated to over 1000 degrees Celsius, resulting in the rock expanding to many times its original volume. Close examination reveals that the expanded product consists of masses of little plates with air pockets between them. It is therefore very light, well aerated and capable of storing significant amounts of available water. An advantage of vermiculite over perlite is its ability to store nutrients due to its chemical makeup. A disadvantage, however, is the tendency for the layers to become recompressed if the medium is compacted too much or mixed when wet. It should also be sterile when it is taken out of its original bag or container. Because of its light weight and excellent water holding capacity, it is often used as a covering for seed. It can be purchased in various particle size grades and, like perlite, its major drawback is its relatively high cost.
- **Plastic foams:** Polystyrene foam of the type used to stuff bean bags is the most readily available. It comes in various particle sizes and does not contain or store any nutrients or water. It is used purely to increase drainage and aeration in the mix, a task it fulfils quite well. It has the disadvantage that larger particles tend to float to the surface of the medium and are easily blown around by wind. It is relatively cheap and may be a useful additive to media for cuttings or for hardening off micropropagated plants.

It is worth looking at the availability and price of the various ingredients in your area before deciding on the sort of medium you are going to use. It is also worth looking at the alternative of buying in a ready-made propagation mix from a reputable potting mix manufacturer. Good quality general potting mixes can be used for some propagation procedures such as seed raising, or they can be blended with any of the above ingredients to form a medium suitable for other propagation techniques. In deciding on a propagation medium, cost is only one consideration, as a low-quality, low-price medium may prove to be a false economy if plant losses are high. The following are some examples of propagation media for different purposes:

Seed sowing mix

Physical:	50% by volume coir fibre ('coconut peat')
	50% by volume fine, lime-free sand
Chemical:	0.75 kg/m³ single superphosphate
	0.4 kg/m³ potassium nitrate
	3.0 kg/m³ calcium carbonate lime.

Semi-hardwood cutting mix

Physical:	40% by volume size 200 perlite
	5% by volume coir fibre ('coconut peat')
	25% by volume coarse washed river sand
Chemical:	2.0 kg/m³ calcium carbonate lime
	1.0 kg/m³ Osmocote Plus® (5–6 month).

Softwood cutting mix

Physical:	30% by volume size 200 perlite
	40% by volume coir fibre ('coconut peat')
	15% by volume coarse washed river sand
	15% by volume vermiculite
Chemical:	2.0 kg/m³ calcium carbonate lime
	1.0 kg/m³ Osmocote Plus® (5–6 month).

Methods of Propagation

For most methods of propagation, standard potting mixes can be used as they have sufficient aeration and water holding capacity. It is advisable, however, to use potting mixes that conform to the premium category of the Australian standards for potting mixes. This should ensure a medium that is free of any physical or chemical defects. In addition, the premium grade will have enough fertiliser to last for a couple of months after potting.

Note: When handling any potting mix, one should observe normally accepted standards of personal hygiene as there may be organisms harmful to humans in the medium. Most notably the organism that causes Legionaire's disease, *Legionella*, is often present. To become infected one must inhale the bacteria. Those particularly at risk are the elderly, smokers or people who have respiratory conditions. It is vital that we bear in mind the idea of keeping the medium moist to avoid air-borne dust and, if necessary, wear a mask to avoid inhalation of dust. Always follow the manufacturer's directions to avoid problems.

The Role of Plant Growth Regulators and Plant Hormones in Plant Propagation

Plant hormones are naturally occurring biochemicals which perform various functions that control the growth and differentiation of plants. The various hormones are produced at sites where active cell division is happening, such as buds, root tips, expanding leaves and fruits. They are active both at those sites and in other parts of the plant to which they are transported, where they perform other controlling functions.

Plant growth regulators are non-nutrient chemicals that control various aspects of plant growth and development. They may be naturally occurring chemicals such as the plant hormones, or they may be synthetic. In other words, all plant hormones are plant growth substances, but not all plant growth substances are hormones.

Root promoting substances—the auxins

A group of plant growth regulators known as auxins is responsible for a wide range of effects on plant growth, including cell enlargement and elongation, phototropism and geotropism, apical dominance, fruit set and growth, seed germination and root initiation.

Auxins for root initiation

There is only one known natural auxin, indoleacetic acid (IAA). Whilst it is a powerful auxin, it is rarely used on cuttings because it breaks down rapidly when exposed to light and non-sterile conditions. In fact, plants produce specific enzymes whose task it is to denature IAA, to stop it reaching excessive levels in plant tissue. Therefore the auxins commonly used in plant propagation are the synthetic types indolebutyric acid (IBA) and naphthalene acetic acid (NAA). These two compounds are very stable and can be stored for long periods of time under appropriate conditions. Auxins can be applied in several ways namely as powder, gel or in aqueous solution.

- **Powders** are probably the most commonly used for commercial cutting production. The auxin concentrate is mixed with finely ground talcum powder, with a wide range of concentrations being available commercially. Most manufacturers offer three types—concentrations of 1000–3000 ppm (parts per million) for softwood cuttings, 3000–8000 ppm for semi-hardwood cuttings and 8000–15 000 ppm for hardwood cuttings. The auxins used are usually either IBA, NAA or a mixture of the two. Bundles of cuttings are prepared and the bottom few millimetres is dipped in the powder. The cuttings are then lightly tapped against the container to remove excess powder before they are planted. There are no hard and fast rules as to which the best auxin or combination is, and it is a matter of trial and error for the individual propagator, according to the species that is being propagated.

- **Gels** which contain auxins and sometimes other substances such as vitamins and other nutrients are available commercially. These are applied in the same way as powders and in my experience are equally as effective. Again they can be based on either IBA, NAA or a mixture of the two and are available in a range of concentrations from 1000 to 15 000 ppm.

- **Aqueous solutions** of auxins can also be prepared by dissolving the auxin and mixing it to the required concentration. The cuttings are then dipped in the solution either for a few seconds for a very high concentration or for a period of 12–24 hours for a low concentration of from 20–200 ppm. Once again, trial and error with different species will reveal the optimal method for the individual propagator.

- **Making up auxin solutions**. The normal auxin concentrates available must have a small amount of alcohol added to them before they will dissolve. This alcohol can sometimes burn the cuttings. Alternatively, a potassium salt of IBA is available commercially which is completely water soluble, and this should be used if aqueous solutions are being prepared.

Rooting Hormones from the Wild Root promoting hormone solutions can be created for nothing by simply taking a number of willow cuttings—either pussy willow (*Salix caprea*) or weeping willow (*S. babylonica*)—and placing them in a jar of water. They will happily produce roots within a couple of weeks, and during this process will release significant amounts of auxin into the water. This solution is then used for soaking the bottoms of any species you desire. A soak of 5–10 minutes should be given for easy to root species, while an hour or so can be used for more difficult to root species.

Gibberellins or gibberellic acids

This group of plant growth regulators is responsible for a variety of plant growth responses, including flower initiation and sex expression, cell division and elongation, fruit set and growth as well as delaying senescence of plant parts. Their most dramatic effect when applied to plants is to cause rapid elongation of stems. Our primary interest in them as propagators is as a means of breaking dormancy in the seeds of various species such as palms. Gibberellins are normally available commercially as aqueous solutions and seed is normally soaked for 24 hours at concentrations ranging from 1000 to 10 000 ppm.

Cytokinins

This group of plant growth regulators is involved in stimulating cell division, cell enlargement and tissue differentiation, as well as breaking down apical dominance in shoot tips. It is used primarily in plant tissue culture media to stimulate multiple shoot formation. For more information on its use, refer to Chapter 10.

Smoke and Seed Germination

The 1990s has been an exciting time for propagators interested in wild-flowers. As detailed later in this appendix, a large number of species from areas prone to bush fires have been shown to have seed germination stimulated by chemical extracts from smoke. Species that had long proven recalcitrant to propagation can now be germinated fairly routinely by these new treatments. We shall start by outlining some simple methods applicable to home gardeners, and then move on to a more detailed look at the scientific research on the subject and how this can be applied to all sorts of situations, from commercial horticultural propagation to bush regeneration *in situ* to rescuing endangered species. Firstly some simple methods:

- **Medium:** As for normal seed raising (see Chapter 3).
- **Container:** As for normal seed raising (see Chapter 3).
- **Method:** Suitable for species such as flannel flower (*Actinotus helianthi*) or kangaroo grass (*Themeda triandra*) and many others. For small quantities of seed a punnet can be used. Make sure the medium has been well watered and is thoroughly moist before sowing the seed. Seed is sown as normal and then a layer of leaf litter a centimetre thick is spread on the surface, to within a centimetre of the edge. Put the container on a non-flammable surface and set fire to the leaf litter, such that it smoulders and smokes rather than burns. The important part is to generate smoke—flames are incidental and not necessary. After the leaf litter has finished smouldering, water very sparingly with a watering can. This latter point is important, as overwatering in the first 24 hours after the treatment can result in leaching out of the active ingredient. Alternatively, smoke extracts can be prepared by bubbling smoke from any type of leaf litter through water until it is discoloured. The extract can then be used

to soak the seed for 24 hours, or used as a drench on the already sown seed, taking care not to water again for at least 24 hours.

- **Propagation environment:** As for normal seed raising.
- **Time of year:** Spring would be a useful starting point unless you have prior knowledge of a better time for sowing the seed.
- **Things to look for in the seed:** It is usually worth dissecting a few seeds of the species in question to make sure they are not hollow or damaged in some other way. Viable seed of many wildflowers can be difficult to obtain, and commercially available seedlots may contain a high percentage of non-viable seed.

Theory of Smoke-Induced Germination

The discovery that smoke-generated chemicals can stimulate germination has revolutionised ideas on the propagation of species which grow naturally in areas where fires are regularly experienced. It has such far-reaching consequences for the propagation and conservation of these species that I have decided to devote an appendix to it. At least three areas of the world have been identified as having numerous species whose seed responds to the chemicals released by smoke, namely the Cape Floral region of South Africa, various fire-prone areas of Australia and the chaparral vegetation areas of southern California. No doubt there are many other areas in Asia, South America and Europe where keen plant propagators could profitably test this powerful new technique. Areas which spring to mind particularly are those places with Mediterranean climates where summer drought is an annual feature of the weather pattern.

This discovery has profound implications for anyone interested in conservation of rare and endangered flora, bush regeneration and plant breeding and domestication of wildflowers. One of the greatest problems in the conservation of plants in fire prone areas, particularly when they occur near inhabited areas, is that the frequency and severity of fires has significantly altered since human settlement. Various methods are being developed to treat soils *in situ* in natural areas so that the natural seed bank can be geminated, thus giving park managers a tool for regenerating and preserving species in fire-prone areas.

A seed smoking unit at Kings Park, Western Australia. Smoke is generated in the drum at the left and is pumped into the tent where seeds are treated in trays or in the soil in situ.

The story of the discovery of the effects of smoke on seed germination and the refinement of the techniques is a fascinating one that stretches over three continents. I think it is worth tracing the scientific work to show how the process has gathered momentum over the last decade or so. The first clues to this discovery were published in the 1980s by Sterling C. Keeley and various co-workers in California. In 1985 a paper was published entitled 'Role of allelopathy, heat and charred wood in the germination of chaparral herbs and suffrutescents' (see J.E. Keeley et al. 1985, in References at the end of this section). This appears to be the first published report that a product of fire was stimulating seed germination rather than the effects of heat. In 1986 Sterling C. Keeley and Marie Pizzorno published a paper entitled 'Charred wood stimulated germination of two fire-following herbs of the California chaparral and the role of hemicellulose' (see References at the end of this section). This paper built on the work of the earlier paper and carried it much further, documenting the 'stimulatory effect on germination of two fire-following chaparral herbs, *Emmenanthe penduliflora* and *Eriophyllum confertiflorum,* of water soluble compounds derived from charred wood of a widespread chaparral shrub'. Keeley and Pizzorno initially tested the effect of extracts from charred wood of *Adenostoma fasciculatum*

Top: *Erica glauca*, a smoke sensitive species from South Africa. Bottom: Results of smoke treatment of Erica seed — left hand tray no treatment, right hand tray smoke treatment. *Neville Brown*

(a member of the rose family) on a range of species, and found this to stimulate germination in species from 15 different families. They then asked whether charred wood extracts from other chaparral and indeed non-chaparral woods would also stimulate germination. The remarkable answer was that it did not seem to matter what type of wood was used. In fact they demonstrated that burning the wood was not necessary, because extracts from wood heated to 175 degrees Celsius in an oven for 30 minutes was similarly effective.

The methods used by Keeley and Pizzorno were rather fascinating. A blow-torch was used to blacken the stems of the wood used, but the torching was stopped before it turned to ash. Baked stem material was also used—stems simply heated at 175 degrees Celsius for 30 minutes without blackening them. Both types of stem were then ground to a powdery consistency. The ground stem material was then used in a few different ways—either sprinkled directly onto seed planted on top of a potting mix or onto seed placed naked in a sterile petri dish, or an aqueous extract was prepared by stirring 2.5 grams of ground, fully charred stems in 20 millilitres of deionized water for 18 hours, then filtered through Whatman No. 1 filter paper. It was found that 24-hour exposure of the seeds to smoke extract was as effective as continual exposure for 14 days. Exposure for less than 24 hours does not appear to have been tested. Keeley and Pizzorno also tested various chemicals from common and more unusual types of wood, and found that heated xylan (a common hemicellulose in plants) and heated glucuronic acid were active ingredients in stimulating germination.

The California chaparral vegetation is similar to that found in drought-prone areas elsewhere in the world, such as large parts of Australia, southern Africa and the Mediterranean region. The plants are characterised by their tough, leathery (sclerophyllous) leaves, which sometimes contain oils which enhance their combustibility. The findings of Keeley and his co-workers suggested that the germination trigger was freely available after a fire and was active on a wide range of species.

Another chapter in this fascinating story then emerged in South Africa in 1990 when J.H. de Lange and C. Boucher published a paper entitled 'Autoecological studies on *Audouinia capitata* (Bruniaceae). I. Plant-derived smoke as a seed germination cue' (see details under References at end of this section). This paper appears to be the first to report the use of smoke derived-chemicals, as opposed to the charred wood used by Keeley et al. De Lange and Boucher report generating smoke by using a 130 litre drum to burn a mixture of fresh and dry plant material from fynbos vegetation. 'The smoke was blown, using bellows, through a pipe into plastic tents erected on nine 0.5 x 0.5 m areas containing seed from different adjoining living mature plants for 30 minutes each. No seedlings were found to germinate in surrounding untreated areas whereas a total of 128 *A. capitata* seedlings were recorded in the nine treated areas after 6 months.' They also prepared an aqueous smoke extract by bubbling smoke through distilled water. This was also found to be effective in stimulating germination of *Audouinia*.

Dr Neville Brown at the Kirstenbosch National Botanic Garden in South Africa wrote the next chapter in the story when he published a paper with the wonderfully readable title 'Promotion of germination of fynbos seeds by plant-derived smoke' (see References at end of this section). This paper detailed the stimulatory effects of smoke and aqueous smoke extracts on seed germination of 18 taxa from such widespread families as Asteraceae, Bruniaceae, Ericaceae, Proteaceae and Restionaceae. Dr Brown took the research a step further by developing a method whereby absorbent paper (such as filter paper) was impregnated with smoke-generated chemicals by passing it through the smoke of (apparently) any sort of fire. The papers are then simply placed in water where they release the active ingredients. The solution thus created can be used either to soak seed directly or to water-in seed sown in a suitable medium. A variation on this technique has been the addition of plant growth regulators or hormones such as cytokinins to the filter paper (Neville Brown, personal communication). An interesting feature of this method is that the concentration of the smoke-generated chemicals can be varied by changing the dilution rate of the solution. In fact, it seems that concentration of the active ingredients can be a critical factor in breaking dormancy of smoke-sensitive species and that too high a concentration of smoke-derived chemicals may even be inhibitory to germination (Brown et al., 1994, see full Reference at the end of this section). For those who wish to take advantage of the research of the experts, there is a tried and tested product which has resulted from the work of Neville Brown at Kirtenbosch Gardens in South Africa. The product has been named Kirstenbosch 'Instant Smoke Plus' Seed Primer, and can be obtained from the Conservation Biology Research Unit at Kirstenbosch by writing to Private Bag X7,

Top: *Rhodocoma capensis* species, a smoke sensitive South African sedge. Bottom: Results of smoke treatment of *Restio* seed left hand tray, right hand tray no treatment.

Claremont, 7735 South Africa (telephone 021 762-3229, fax 021 762-3229). In Australia the product is available from D. Oriell Seed Exporters, 45 Frape Avenue, Mt Yokine, Perth, Western Australia, 6060.

Dr Brown has also identified that smoke treatments may need to be combined with other treatments to break dormancy in some species. For instance, he recommends that nut-fruited species of Restionaceae from the Cape region of South Africa should be heated to 120 degrees Celsius for 3 minutes prior to smoke treatment.

Subsequently workers in Western Australia, led by Dr Kingsley Dixon at Kings Park and Botanic Garden, began to test this exciting new research on the fire-prone flora in their care. In 1995 Dixon, Shauna Roche and John Pate published 'The promotive effect of smoke derived from burnt native vegetation on seed germination of Western Australian plants' (see References at the end of this section). They found that smoke treatment enhanced germination in 45 out of 94 species from 21 different plant families, ranging from monocotyledons to dicotyledons and even one gymnosperm (*Actinostrobus acuminatus*). All these species had been classified as very difficult, if not impossible, to germinate in cultivation prior to this work.

Dixon and his co-workers used the 'smoke tent' and aqueous smoke extract techniques of the South Africans. They also developed a 'smoked filter paper' technique by 'hanging dry, 9 cm Whatman Seed Testing Papers (no. 182) in the fumigation tent and exposing to smoke for 90 minutes'. Seeds were placed onto the filter papers to test germination and this teatment also gave positive responses. Yet another technique was used in the field where a one-centimetre layer of fine dry quartz sand was fumigated in the smoke tent for 90 minutes. The sand was then spread over bushland plots under study. Smoked sand was effective, but not as good as smoked water. Considerable variation was found between different species in their response to the various treatments. This led to the conclusion that 'seed banks of certain species may have to react sequentially and possibly additively to a number of stimuli before specific members become committed to germinate'. In other words, while smoke-related chemicals are a large part of the story in fire-prone areas, they are by no means the whole story and propagators must keep an open mind about trying combinations of dormancy-breaking treatments.

More recently Kingsley Dixon and his team at King's Park in Perth have pioneered a method where a bulk quantity of smoke-impregnated water is collected in a tanker and is sprayed on to areas to be regenerated, thus dispensing with the need for the cumbersome equipment involved in 'smoke tents'.

Summary of Smoke-Induced Germination

What sort of smoke is required?

Perhaps a natural response to this question would be that the smoke should be generated by the combustion of dried vegetation of the species itself or at least from the plant community that it belongs to. This approach has certainly been successful for most species. However, it also appears that for many species suitable smoke can be generated from just about any sort of cellulose, source even including something as mundane as newspaper (Neville Brown, personal communication). This observation was made on research done with South African species, so whether this applies to all smoke-sensitive species in other parts of the world remains to be seen. The work in California mentioned earlier suggests that it will be so.

How should the smoke be applied?

An interesting aspect of the smoke phenomenon is that it explains the success of a practice that has long been recommended for the germination of flannel flower (*Actinotus helianthi*). The technique involves sowing seed as normal in a seed tray and then piling leaf litter on top and burning it. I have found this method to be extremely successful and it would appear that smoke-generated chemicals were the active ingredient in breaking seed dormancy. This method can therefore be recommended as a viable technique, especially in small-scale situations such as home gardens.

A number of methods have been successfully employed to bring the active ingredients from smoke into contact with the seeds. The most obvious method is to plant the seed in a suitable medium in a seed tray and then expose the tray and its contents to artificially-generated smoke, usually produced from some convenient smoke-generating device such as an apiarist's smoker.

Another exciting application for this knowldge is for rehabilation of disturbed landscapes such as mining sites. To quote Brown et al., 1994 (see Reference page 195): 'Two approaches can be followed in applying smoke technology to the situation in restoration ecology. The first approach is to pretreat seed of the species to be used in the revegetation process before sowing. The second approach is to treat the actual site to stimulate germination of seeds in the natural seed bank in the topsoil or alternatively stimulate germination of seeds that have been sown in the soil. In the first approach seeds may be smoke-treated immediately before sowing or they may be treated some time before and stored under appropriate conditions (for a limited period) until sown. Smoke treatment may be actual smoking, soaking in aqueous solution of smoke or soaking in an aqueous solution of charred wood before sowing. In the second option seed in the topsoil (natural seed bank or sown seed) can be terated in a number of ways: (i) by direct smoking, using a polythene-film smoke tent, or (ii) by spraying aqueous smoke solution, or (iii) by irrigation of plots with aqueous smoke solution (or alternatively, an aqueous solution of charred wood may be used).'

Can smoke treatments be applied in the field without burning the area?

Yes, most definitely. Early research centred on putting up plastic tents and then injecting smoke into them and leaving this for at least 24 hours. Later work has seen smoke-treated water applied directly to the soil in areas being regenerated.

Can smoke treated seed be stored and successfully sown later?

The ever-increasing interest in retaining genetic diversity in plant communities worldwide has led to propagators collecting indigenous seed from localised plant communities and using this for regeneration works. Often the scale of work required and limited availability of funds dictates that the seed be sown directly into the site to be regenerated, rather than being propagated in pots first. This direct sowing approach meets with varying success, with large seeded legumes such as acacias often being the easiest to establish. For fire prone areas it would seem that smoke treatments will have obvious applications for these direct sowing operations. A study on a South African grass, *Themeda triandra*, showed not only that smoke treating seed promoted germination, but also that the smoke-treated seed could be stored for up to 21 days and still retain this improvement. This suggests that it may be possible to develop smoke pretreatments for sensitive seed that will be applicable to the direct sowing of extensive areas. In other words, it will be highly worthwhile to experiment with smoke-sensitive species by treating seed in bulk and then drying it for sowing over a period of time.

What are the active ingredients in smoke?

It is still unclear what the active ingredients are. It would seem likely that a combination of chemicals is involved, as smoke extracts which have been analysed show a cocktail of dozens of different compounds and to date no single chemical has been able to elicit the same response as the 'cocktail' does.

Are there any other factors which interact with smoke chemicals such as hormones, temperature, moisture, nicking of seeds etc?

Research with various South African species has shown that other important cues include alternating germination temperatures, dry (smokeless) heat, ethylene, ammonia and seed storage temperature. The growth regulators GA_4 and GA_7 (gibberellic acids) can be substituted for smoke in breaking dormancy in some species. In *Syncarpha vestita*, light inhibited germination, darkness promoted germination and smoke overcame the effects of light. In the hard-seeded South African legume *Cyclopia intermedia* there was a 40 per cent increase in germination following a 24-hour soak in 1:320 dilution of smoke extract in water, after the seed had first been acid scarified to break down the hard seed coat.

It would seem that for many species a series of environmental cues are required, sometimes in a particular order, while in other species smoke is the major trigger on its own. Researchers working with particular species obviously need to carefully examine the natural environment to look for cues which may interact with smoke treatments.

What is the importance of this discovery to horticulture?

There are many spectacular wildflowers in fire prone areas around the world. Many of these species are highly sought-after as cut flowers, and a flourishing worldwide trade has developed in flowers picked from the wild. Examples include the proteas (*Protea* species) of South Africa, kangaroo paws (*Anigozanthos* species) and feather flowers (*Verticordia* species) of Western Australia, and the flannel flower (*Actinotus helianthi*) of eastern Australia. Picking of such species from the wild is obviously an undesirable way to supply the commercial trade as the removal of the choicest specimens not only reduces the overall seed supply in the wild but also skews the gene pools of the plant's population towards the inferior types left behind. In addition, wild picked material is often damaged and does not usually give high quality flowers.

Cultivation of the wildflowers mentioned above (all of which come from fire-prone areas) has often been hindered by unreliable propagation. Flannel flower provides a great example of how smoke-induced germination may play a crucial role in successful cultivation, resulting in a reduction in exploitation of wild populations. The flannel flower is a short-lived perennial that is probably best grown as an annual or biennial in cultivation. It has proven difficult to establish in cultivation because of unreliable germination, and poor success in transplanting established seedlings into the field situation. As this species has already demonstrated a response to smoke treatment, a very worthwhile avenue of research could be to pretreat seed and then sow it directly into the field.

Smoke treatments also offer considerable promise to would-be breeders of responsive plant species. A much higher rate of recovery of hybrid seedlings should be achievable, giving breeders a much greater diversity from which to select new cultivars.

I have tried smoke treatments but have had limited success. Are there any factors which may cause problems for propagators?

The chemicals released by the smoke are water soluble and thus it is possible for them to be leached from around the seeds if overwatering occurs. To avoid problems it would appear that watering should be sparing for 24–48 hours after smoke treatments have been applied.

List of species, arranged by family, in which treatment with smoke or aqueous smoke extract has been shown to give improved germination (courtesy D. Oriell Seed Exporters).

Anthericaceae: *Thysanotus multiflorus*

Apiaceae: *Actinotus helianthi*

Apocynaceae: *Alyxia buxifolia*

Asteraceae: *Edmondia sesamoides, Helichrysum patulum* (syn. *H. crispum*), *Helichrysum foetidum, Ixodia achilleoides, Metalasia densa* (syn. *M. muricata*), *Othonna quinque-dentata, Phaenocoma prolifera, Syncarpha speciosissima, S. vestita* (syn. *Helichrysum vestitum*), *S. eximia* (syn. *Helipterum eximium*), *Senecio grandiflorus:*

Bruniaceae: *Audouinia capitata,Berzelia lanuginosa]*

Campanulaceae: *Lobelia* species

Chloanthaceae: *Lachnostachys eriobotrya*

Colchicaceae: *Burchardia umbellata*

Cupressaceae: *Actinostrobus acuminatus, Widdringtonia cupressioides* (syn. *W. nodiflora*)

Dilleniaceae: *Hibbertia amplexicaulis, Hibbertia lasiopus, Hibbertia quadricolor, Hibbertia sericea*

Epacridaceae: *Leucopogon parniflorus, Lysinema ciliatum, Sphenotoma capitatum, Styphelia* species affinis *pulchella*

Ericaceae: *Erica caffra, Erica canaliculata, Erica capensis, Erica capitata, Erica cerinthoides, Erica clavisepala, Erica curvrostris, Erica deflexa, Erica diaphana, Erica dilatata, Erica discolor, Erica ericoides, Erica formosa, Erica glauca var. elegans, Erica glauca var. glauca, Erica glomiflora, Erica grata, Erica hebecalyx, Erica hirtiflora, Erica junonia var. minor, Erica lateralis, Erica latiflora, Erica longifolia, Erica nudiflora, Erica oatesii, Erica perlata, Erica phylicifolia, Erica pinea, Erica plukenetii, Erica recta, Erica sphaeroidea, Erica spectabilis, Erica simulans, Erica sitiens, Erica taxifolia, Erica thomae, Erica tumida, Erica turgida, Erica vestita*

Fabaceae: *Cyclopia intermedia*

Geraniaceae: *Pelargonium auritum, Pelargonium capitatum, Pelargonium crithmifolium*

Goodeniaceae: *Lechenaultia floribunda, Lechenaultia formosa, Lechenaultia macrantha, Scaevola calliptera, Velleia rosea*

Haemodoraceae: *Anigozanthos bicolor, Anigozanthos humilis, Anigozanthos manglesii, Conostylis setosa*

Iridaceae: *Patersonia occidentalis*

Lamiaceae: *Hemiandra pungens*

Malvaceae: *Alyogyne heakeifolia, Alyogyne huegelii*

Myrtaceae: *Hypocalymma angustifolium, Verticordia densiflora:*

Let's Propagate!

Pittosporaceae: *Billardiera bicolor*

Poaceae: *Neurachne alopecuroidea, Themeda triandra*

Proteaceae: *Aulax cancellata, Conospermum incurvum, Conospermum triplinervum, Dryandra* species, *Grevillea wilsonii, Isopogon* species, *Persoonia longifolia, Petrophile drummondii, Protea compacta, Serruria florida, Serruria phylicoides, Stirlingia latiifolia*

Restionaceae: *Askidiosperma andreanum, Cannomois virgata, Chondro-petalum hookerianum, Chondropetalum mucronatum, Chondropetalum tectorum, Dovea macrocarpa, Elegia capensis, Elegia cuspidata, Elegia fenestrata, Ischyrolepis sieberi, Ischyrolepis subverticillata, Restio brachiatus, Restio festuciformis, Restio praeacutus, Restio similis, Restio tetragonus, Restio triticeus, Rhodocoma capensis, Rhodocoma gigantea, Staberoha aemula, Staberoha cernua, Staberoha distachya, Staberoha vaginata, Thamnochortus bachmannii, Thamnochortus cinereus, Thamnochortus ebracteatum, Thamnochortus pellcidus, Thamnochortus punctatus, Thamnochortus spicigerus, Thamnochortus sporadeus*

Rutaceae: *Eriostemon spicatus, Geleznowia verrucosa.*

Propagation of Commonly Encountered Plants

This is not intended to be a comprehensive encyclopedia, rather it brings together the experience of the author in a range of plants under Australian conditions and describes exceptions to the rule for particular genera, in order to help the reader avoid some of the pitfalls that may be encountered. Australian native plants are shown in Table 1, and selected exotics in Table 2. (SHW indicates semi-hardwood.)

Table 1:

Propagation Methods for Australian Native Plants

Plant name	Propagation method	Time of year
Acacia species (Wattle)	Seed is shed as soon as the pod(legume) is ripe.	Spring preferably but other times of year OK
	SHW cuttings	Autumn
	Seed keeps extremely well, even at room temperature. Scarification is required to break through the hard seed coat. Perhaps the best method is to pour boiling water over the seed and allow it to stand for 24 hours to imbibe water. Seed normally germinates rapidly. Cultivars such as *Acacia baileyana* 'Purpurea' and 'Prostrata' are best propagated by cuttings using 3000 ppm IBA.	
Acmena and *Syzigium* (Lilly pillies)	Seed	Spring
	SHW cuttings	Autumn
	The fleshy fruits (drupes) come in a range of colours when ripe, including white , red, purple and pink. Using secateurs, cut off the small branchlets bearing the fruits and strip the	

fruits into a bowl or large glass container and use the maceration method of seed extraction. Seed should be sown fresh.

Actinodium cunninghamii	SHW cuttings	Autumn
(Swamp Daisy)	Use standard methods for semi-hardwood cuttings	

Actinotus helianthi	Seed	Autumn or spring
(Flannel Flower)	Softwood cuttings	Autumn
	Seed germination is greatly enhanced with smoke treatment. cuttings of non-flowering shoots can be treated with 1000 ppm IBA and given 25°C bottom heat.	

Adenanthos species	SHW cuttings	Autumn
	Seed is rarely obtainable. SHW cuttings with standard rates of auxin have given reasonable results.	

Adiantum species	Division	Late winter
(Maiden Hair Ferns)	Spores	All year
	Divide as plants are coming into new growth in late winter. Spores are sown on sphagnum peat and a layer of cling wrap plastic placed over the container to raise humidity levels. Development of mature plants may take many months.	

Aegiceras corniculatum	Seed	All year
(River Mangrove)	Seed actually germinates on the plant and live seedlings can be harvested underneath the tree and easily transplanted. Seedlings tolerate very high salt levels.	

Agathis species	Seed	Spring
(Kauri Pines)	Seed germinates freely but needs warm conditions.	

Agonis species	*Method as for Callistemon.*	

Allocasuarina and	Seed	Spring
Casuarina species	For most species the seed is held on the plant indefinitely. However a couple of species (*A. cunninghamii* and *A. leuhmannii*) shed seed annually in autumn and must therefore be closely watched. Seed can be stored for many years even at room temperature. Seed should germinate within several weeks with no dormancy problems.	
(She Oaks)		

Alpinia species	Seed	Spring
(Native Gingers)	Division	Spring
	Seed may take several months to germinate—no special pretreatment required.	

Ammobium alatum	Seed	Spring
(Winged Everlasting)	Division	Spring

	Use standard methods.	
***Angophora* species**	Seed	Autumn to spring
(Apple Gums)	The fruit is a woody capsule but unlike the eucalypts it opens as soon as the seed is ripe and sheds its seed. This can happen quite quickly and it may be best to actually bag the fruits on the tree with old stockings. The only drawback is that it may be difficult to reach the capsules on some species, given the height of the lower branches. In this case a tarpaulin spread under the tree is an alternative, but far less efficient. The individual seeds are quite large and ger minate quite readily and can be stored reasonably well.	
***Anigozanthos* species and hybrids**	Seed	Spring
	Division	Autumn
(Kangaroo paws)	Micropropagation	All year round
	Fruit is a capsule which splits open at the top as soon as the seed is ripe. The capsules remain upright and as such retain a lot of the seed indefinitely. Seed of some species germi nates freely without any treatment, e.g *A. flavidus*. Several species have responded to smoke treatments, namely *A. manglesii, A. bicolor* and *A. humilis*. Given that most of the other species come from fire-prone heath or woodland, it would be a safe bet that these will also be responsive to smoke treatment. Division is a possibility for species that are reasonably long-lived, notably *A. flavidus* and the numer ous hybrid cultivars bred from it. Autumn is the best time to divide and the foliage should be reduced by about a half before the divisions are potted up. Commercially, kangaroo paw hybrids are done by micropropagation as the space required to hold parent stock for division is prohibitive for most nurseries.	
***Araucaria* species**	Seed	Spring
(Bunya Pine, Norfolk Island Pine, Hoop Pine)	The large, edible seeds of the Bunya pine are so big that they can be planted half out of the medium. This way the weight of the seed keeps it in place and signs of germination can be easily observed. Other species should be done accord ing to normal seed methods.	
***Archontophoenix* species**	Seed	All year
(Alexander and	Seed should be sown fresh and germination may take 6–12	

Bangalow Palms)	months. Gibberellic acid treatment may be beneficial.	
***Asplenium* species**	Spores	All year
(Bird's Nest & Hen & Chicken Fern)	See notes on *Adiantum*.	
***Astartea* species**	Seed	Spring
	SHW cuttings	Autumn
	Collect seed capsules when ripe. Use standard SHW cutting techniques.	
***Atriplex* species**	Seed	Spring
(Saltbushes)	Softwood cuttings	Spring
	Use standard techniques.	
***Austromyrtus* species**	Seed	Autumn
	SHW cuttings	Autumn
	Sow seed immediately after harvest. Use standard techniques.	
***Backhousia* species**	Seed	Spring
	SHW cuttings	Autumn
	Use standard techniques. Cuttings may be slow to strike.	
***Baeckea* species**	Seed	Spring
	SHW cuttings	Autumn
	As for *Astartea* spp.	
***Banksia* species**	Seed	Spring
	SHW cuttings	Autumn
	Grafting (top cleft)	Late winter

The 'flower' of a Banksia is actually a collection of hundreds of individual flowers and usually only a handful of those flowers mature to produce the seed-bearing woody fruits (follicles). The woody structures protect the seed in a bushfire and most species are adapted to holding their seed on the plant indefinitely and only releasing when the branch or whole plant dies. For these species, mature cones are collected and heated in an oven at 100°C until the follicles open, which usually takes 15–20 minutes. Or, for the more adventurous, a blowtorch can be used to singe the cones. Opening of the follicles generally occurs soon after this treatment. It should be noted that not all Banksias retain the seed on the plant indefinitely, rather the follicles open as soon as the seed is ripe. Such species include *B. integrifolia*, *B. grandis* and *B. marginata*. Note also that each follicle contains a woody divider (which is sometimes mistaken for the seed) between the 2 seeds it normally contains. The actual seeds are quite small and have a wispy membranous wing attached to them.

Bauera species	SHW cuttings	Autumn
(Dog Rose)	Simple layering	Spring/summer
	Use standard methods. Bend low growing branches down and bury them with the tip uncovered.	

Beaufortia species	Seed	Spring
	SHW cuttings	Autumn
	Seed capsules take about a year to mature on the plant. Seed can be stored for years. Use standard methods for cuttings.	

| *Billardiera* species | Soft tip and SHW cuttings | Spring to Autumn |
| | Use standard methods. | |

Blandfordia species	Seed	Spring
(Xmas Bells)	Division	Spring
	Use standard methods. Use standard methods.	

Blechnum species	Spores	Spring
	Division	Spring
	See *Adiantum* for method for seed. Use standard methods for division.	

Boronia species	Seed	Spring
	Softwood or SHW cuttings	Summer to Autumn
	Western Australian species such as Brown Boronia (*B. megastigma*) are readily propagated by seed. Some species have responded to smoke treatment. Softwood or semi-hardwood cuttings are successful for most species and cultivars using standard hormone treatments and bottom heat at 25°C.	

Bossiaea species	Seed	All year
	SHW cuttings	Autumn
	Place seed in boiling water and soak for 24 hours. Some species have been readily done by standard methods for SHW cuttings.	

| *Brachychiton* species | Seed | Spring preferably |
| | Fruits are large woody capsules that split open when the seed is ripe. Preferably collect the fruits before they open and place in a paper bag in a warm, dry place to open. The seed can be tapped out or gently eased out with a pencil or similar. Beware of irritant hairs within the fruit similar to | |

those encountered with Norfolk Island hibiscus *(Lagunaria patersonii)*. Seed stores for a couple of years but is best sown fresh with no pretreatment.

Brachycome species	Soft tip cuttings	All year
	Use standard methods.	
Brachysema species	Seed	All year
	SHW cuttings	Autumn
	Place seed in boiling water and soak for 24 hours. Some species have been readily done by standard methods for SHW cuttings.	
Buckinghamia celsissima	Seed	Spring
(Ivory Curl)	SHW cuttings	Autumn
	Seed germinates best when fresh but will store for a few years. Use standard methods.	
Callicarpa serratifolia	Seed	Spring
(Black Wattle)	Seed must be collected as soon as it matures and should be sown fresh.	
Callistemon species	Seed	Spring/Summer
and cultivars	SHW cuttings	Autumn
(Bottlebrush)	Fruits are woody capsules which are, for most (but not all) species, retained with the seed on the plant indefinitely. This makes seed collection particularly easy as capsules are simply removed from the plant and placed in a paper bag and left in a warm, dry place. Use standard techniques for cuttings.	
Callitris species	Seed	Spring to summer
(Native Cypress Pines)	Seed is held in the cones indefinitely. Cones are harvested and left in a warm, dry place where they will open. Seed lasts for a few years if stored dry.	
Calocephalus brownii	Soft tip cuttings	All year round
(Cushion Bush)	Use standard methods.	
Calomeria amaranthoides	Seed	Spring
(Incense Plant)	Seed responds very well to smoke treatments. A biennial plant that can also be propagated by soft tip cuttings.	
Calothamnus species	Seed	Spring
(One-sided Bottle Brush)	SHW cuttings	Autumn
	As for Callistemon *spp.*	
Calytrix species	Soft tip or SHW cuttings	Summer to Autumn

	Use standard techniques.	
Cassinia species	Soft tip cuttings	Spring to summer
(Curry Bushes)	Use standard techniques.	
Castanospermum	Seed	All year round
australe	This fascinating rainforest tree has highly ornamental pods	
(Black Bean Tree)	(legumes) with very large seeds in them. These seeds should	
	be sown fresh (as for most rainforest species) and only half-	
	embedded in the medium.	
Casuarina species	Seed	Spring to Autumn
(She Oaks)	*See* Allocasuarina.	
Ceratopetalum	Seed	Autumn
gummiferum	SHW cuttings	Autumn
(NSW Christmas Bush)	This plant has traditionally been grown from seed. The fruits	
	contain a single seed and should be harvested just after the	
	showy calyx turns from red to brown. The whole fruit is then	
	sown as though it were a seed as soon as possible after it is	
	harvested. Germination takes several weeks normally. Selected	
	forms such as 'Albery's Red' are propagated by cuttings taken	
	in early to late autumn at the semi-hardwood stage. Cuttings	
	strike with some difficulty and may take several months.	
Chamelaucium species	Soft tip or SHW cuttings	Spring to Autumn
(Wax Flowers)	Use standard methods.	
Chorizema cordatum	Seed or STC	Spring
(Coral Pea)	Scarification treatment needed for seed. Soaking in boiling	
	water is very effective.	
Cissus species	Seed	Spring to summer
(Native Grapes)	Soft tip cuttings	Spring
	Use standard techniques for cuttings. Sow seed fresh using	
	standard techniques	
Clematis species	Soft tip cuttings	Spring to summer
	Use standard techniques.	
Clianthus (Swainsona)	Seed	Spring
formosus	Scarify seed with sandpaper and sow using standard	
(Sturt's Desert Pea)	techniques.	
Comesperma species	Seed	Spring
(Native Milkworts)	SHW cuttings	Spring
	Use standard techniques.	
Conospermum species	Seed	Spring

(Smokebushes)	Smoke treatments have been successful for several species and are worth trying for all species. Propagation by SHW cuttings is possible but difficult for most species.	
Conostylis species	Seed or division	Autumn
(Cotton Heads)	Seed generally has a low germination rate and it would be worth trying smoke treatment. When dividing make sure that pieces have at least several shoots.	
Cordyline species	Seed	Spring to Summer
(Palm Lilies)	Hardwood cuttings	Spring to Autumn
	Sow seed fresh in warm moist conditions. Use standard methods for cuttings.	
Correa species	Softwood to SHW cuttings	Summer to autumn
	Use standard methods.	
Corynanthera flava	SHW cuttings	Autumn
	Use standard methods.	
Craspedia species	Seed	Autumn
(Billy Buttons)	Softwood cuttings	Spring
	Use standard methods.	
Crinum species	Seed	Summer
	Separation	Autumn
	Seed often germinates while still on the plant, therefore sow seed fresh. Bulblets can be removed and potted up.	
Crowea species	Softwood to SHW cuttings	Summer to Autumn
	Use standard methods. Try to find cuttings that do not have flowers or buds.	
Cryptandra species	SHW cuttings	Autumn
	Use standard methods.	
Cupaniopsis anacardioides	Seed	Spring
(Tuckeroo)	Seed should be sown fresh. Use standard methods.	
Curcuma australasica	Division	Spring
(Cape York Lily)	Divide as plants show signs of new growth in spring. Use standard methods.	
Cuttsia viburnea	Seed	Spring
(Native Elderberry)	SHW cuttings	Autumn
	Use standard methods.	
Cyathea species	Spore	Spring
(Tree Ferns)	See *Adiantum* for details.	
Cycas species	Seed	Anytime

(Cycads)	Sow seed fresh. Seed may take many months to germinate. Leave seed half exposed when planted.	
Cymbidium species	Division	After flowering
	Seed	Anytime
	Each division should have a pseudobulb with at least one or 2 active shoots. Seed is propagated by tissue culture methods.	
Cymbopogon refractus (Barbed Wire Grass)	Seed	Spring
	Use standard methods.	
Cyperus species (Sedges)	Division	All year
	Seed	Spring
	Use standard methods.	
Dampiera species	Softwood cuttings	Spring to summer
	Leaf cuttings	Spring
	Use standard methods. Some success has been achieved with leaf cuttings for species such as *D. wellsiana* that have a basal rosette habit of growth.	
Danthonia species (Wallaby Grasses)	Division	Autumn
	Seed	Anytime
	Divisions should be established in pots first. Seed does not germinate well when fresh and should be stored for at least a year before sowing.	
Darlingia species (Silky Oaks)	Seed	Spring to summer
	SHW cuttings	Autumn
	Seed should be sown fresh. Use standard methods. Use standard methods for cuttings, which may take many months to strike.	
Darwinia species	SHW cuttings	Autumn
	Use standard methods.	
Davallia pyxidata (Hare's Foot Fern)	Division	Spring
	Spores	Spring
	Use standard methods. See *Adiantum* for methods.	
Davidsonia pruriens (Davidson's Plum)	Seed	Spring
	Seed should be sown fresh.	
Daviesia species	Seed	Spring
	Boiling water treatment should be used before sowing.	
Dendrobium species	Division	Spring
	Seed	Any time

Each division should be substantial with at least 4–5 shoots per clump. Seed is propagated with some difficulty by tissue culture methods.

Dianella species	Division	
(Flax Lilies)	Seed	Autumn
	Use standard methods for division. Sow seed fresh. Use standard methods.	
Dichondra repens	Seed	Spring
(Kidney Plant)	Division	Anytime
	Use standard methods.	
Dicksonia antarctica	Spore	Spring
(Soft Tree Fern)	See *Adiantum* for method. This species is often transplanted by cutting off the top and planting it. Unfortunately the bottom will not regrow and therefore this is not a propagation option.	
Dillwynia species	Seed	Spring
(Parrot Peas)	Softwood to SHW cuttings	Summer to Autumn
	Boiling water treatment is necessary before sowing. Use standard methods for cuttings.	
Diploglottis species	Seed	Spring
(Native Tamarinds)	Seed should be sown fresh.	
Dodonaea species	Seed	Spring
(Hop Bushes)	Softwood to SHW cuttings	Summer to Autumn
	Boiling water treatment is necessary before sowing. Use standard methods.	
Doodia aspera	Division	Spring
(Rasp Fern)	Spore	Anytime
	Use standard methods. See *Adiantum* for spore method.	
Doryanthes excelsa	Seed	Spring
(Gymea Lily)	Division	Autumn to spring
	Use standard methods.	
Doryphora sassafras	Seed	Spring
(Sassafras)	Seed should be sown fresh.	
Drosera species	Seed	Spring
(Sundews)	Leaf cuttings	Spring
	Sow seed fresh and use a medium of pure peat moss. Use whole leaf and petiole and use standard leaf cutting method.	
Dryandra species	Seed	Spring
	Softwood toSHW cuttings	Autumn

Many species respond to smoke treatment. Use standard methods for cuttings.

Elaeocarpus reticulatus	SHW cuttings	Autumn
(Blueberry Ash)	Seed	Spring

Use standard methods for cuttings. Seed should be sown fresh and may take many months to germinate.

***Epacris* species**	Softwood cuttings	Spring
(Heaths)	Use standard methods.	

***Eremaea* species**	Seed	Spring
	Softwood to SHW cuttings	Summer to Autumn
	Grafting	Winter

Use standard methods. Some species strike readily, others may take many months. *Kunzea ambigua* has been successful as a rootstock for *E. beaufortioides* using the top cleft method.

***Eremophila* species**	Seed	Spring
(Emu Bushes)	Softwood to SHW cuttings	Summer to Autumn
	Grafting	Winter

Germination is erratic and there are unsolved dormancy problems in this genus. Sow seed fresh and be prepared to wait months for results. For cuttings, use low-level auxin treatments e.g. 1000 ppm IBA. *Myoporum insulare* and *M. montanum* have been successfully used as rootstocks for a wide range of species.

***Eriostemon* species**	Seed	Spring
(Wax Flowers)	SHW cuttings	Autumn

Seed of some species has responded to smoke treatment. Breaking the hard seed coat before applying smoke treatment may further enhance results. Use standard methods.

***Eucalyptus* species**	Seed	Spring
	Softwood to SHW cuttings	Summer
	Aerial layering	Autumn

Use standard methods. Cuttings need to be taken from vigorous, rejuvenated shoots from the base of cut-back trees. Material from older trees rarely strikes due to chemical inhibitors. Success has been achieved with a few species.

***Euodia* species**	Seed	Spring to Summer
(Evodias)		

Sow seed fresh. Germination is often erratic and can take many months.

***Euphrasia* species**	Seed	Spring to Autumn
(Eyebrights)	Sow seed fresh. Germination may be enhanced by soaking seed in gibberellic acid solution for several hours.	

***Eutaxia* species**	SHW cuttings	Autumn
	Seed	Spring
	Use standard methods for cuttings. Seed should be treated with boiling water before sowing.	

***Ficus* species** (Figs)	SHW cuttings	Autumn
	Aerial layering	Spring
	Use standard methods.	

***Flindersia* species**	Seed	Spring
(Silkwoods)	Sow seed fresh. Use standard methods.	

***Gahnia* species**	Seed	All Year
	Division	Autumn
	Seed germinates erratically. Smoke treatment may be worth trialling. Use standard methods.	

***Gastrolobium* species**	Seed	Spring
(Poison Peas)	Seed should be treated with boiling water before sowing. Use standard methods.	

***Geijera* species**	Seed	Spring
(Wilgas)	Sow fresh seed. Use standard methods. Germination is often erratic.	

Geleznowia verrucosa	Seed	Autumn
(Yellow Bells)	Seed responds to smoke treatment.	

***Geranium* species**	Softwood cuttings	Spring to Summer
(Crane's Bills)	Use standard methods.	

***Gleichenia* species**	Spore	All year
(Coral Ferns)	See *Adiantum* for details.	

Glochidion ferdinandii	Seed	Spring
(Cheese Tree)	Seed must be sown fresh. Use standard methods.	

***Gompholobium* species**	Seed	Spring
(Wedge Peas)	SHW Cutting	Autumn
	Seed should be treated with boiling water before sowing. Use standard methods.	

***Goodenia* species**	Seed	Spring to Summer
	Softwood cuttings	Spring to Summer
	Seed is difficult to collect as it is shed as soon as it is ripe. Use standard methods. Germination may be erratic. Use	

standard methods for cuttings.

Gossypium sturtianum	Seed	Spring
(Sturt's Desert Rose)	Softwood cuttings	Spring
	Use standard methods.	
***Graptophyllum* species**	SHW cuttings	Autumn
(Native Fuchsias)	Use standard methods.	
***Grevillea* species**	Seed	Spring
	SHW cuttings	Autumn
	Use standard methods. Remove soft tips and flower buds if present.	
***Guichenotia* species**	SHW cuttings	Autumn
	Use standard methods.	
***Haeckeria* species**	Seed	Spring
	SHW cuttings	Autumn
	Sow seed fresh. Use standard methods.	
***Haemodorum* species**	Seed	Spring to Summer
(Bloodroots)	Division	Autumn
	Sow seed fresh. Seed may respond to smoke treatment. Sow seed fresh. Use standard methods.	
***Hakea* species**	Seed	Spring
	SHW cuttings	Autumn
	Grafting	Late winter
	Use standard methods. Grafting succesful for a wide range of species. Top cleft graft is used for *H. bucculenta*, *H. francisciana* and *H. multilineata which* are all grafted onto *H. salicifolia.*	
***Hardenbergia* species**	Seed	Spring to Autumn
(Native Sarsparillas)	Softwood cuttings	Spring
	Seed should be soaked in boiling water before sowing. Use standard methods for cuttings. Cultivars must be propagated by cuttings.	
***Harpullia* species**	Seed	Spring
(Tulipwoods)	Sow seed fresh. Use standard methods.	
Helichrysum Bracteantha	Seed	Autumn
(*Straw Flower*)	Softwood cuttings	Spring
	Use standard methods.	
***Heliotropium* species**	Seed	Spring
	Use standard methods.	

***Helipterum* species**	Seed	Autumn
(some are now	Softwood cuttings	Spring to Summer
Rhodanthe spp)	Use standard methods. Cuttings are used for perennial species.	
Helmholtzia glaberrima	Division	Autumn
(Stream Lily)	Seed	Autumn
	Use standard methods. Sow seed fresh. Use standard methods.	
***Hemiandra* species**	Seed	Spring
(Snakebushes)	Use standard methods.	
***Hibbertia* species**	Softwood cuttings	Spring to Summer
(Guinea Flowers)	Use standard methods.	
***Hibiscus* species**	SHW cuttings	Autumn
	Use standard methods.	
***Homoranthus* species**	SHW cuttings	Autumn
	Use standard methods.	
***Hovea* species**	Seed	Spring
	Seed should be soaked in boiling water before sowing.	
***Hoya* species**	Softwood cuttings	Spring to Autumn
	Use standard methods. Single node cuttings are very successful.	
Hymenosporum flavum	Seed	Spring
(Native Frangipani)	Use standard methods. Seed retains viability for up to 2 years after collection.	
***Hypocalymma* species**	SHW cuttings	Autumn
	Use standard methods.	
Imperata cylindrica	Division	Spring to Autumn
(Blady Grass)	Use standard methods.	
***Indigofera* species**	Seed	Spring to Summer
(Indigos)	Seed should be soaked in boiling water before sowing. Seed is difficult to collect.	
***Ipomoea* species**	Seed	Spring to Autumn
(Morning Glories)	Softwood cuttings	Spring
	Use standard methods.	
***Isopogon* species**	Seed	Spring to Summer
(Coneflowers, Drumsticks)	SHW cuttings	Autumn
	Seed of many species responds to smoke treatment. Use standard methods for cuttings.	
***Isotoma* species**	Seed	Autumn
(Isotomes)	Use standard methods. Sow seed fresh.	

Ixodia achilleoides	Seed	Spring to Autumn
	SHW cuttings	Autumn
	Smoke treatment would be worth trying. Use standard methods. Germination can be erratic. Use standard method for cuttings.	
Jacksonia species	Seed	Spring to Summer
	Seed should be soaked in boiling water before sowing.	
Jasminum species	Softwood cuttings	Spring to Summer
(Jasmines)	Use standard methods.	
Johnsonia lupulina	Seed	Autumn
(Hooded Lily)	Use standard methods. Germiantion may take many months	
Juncus species	Division	Spring to Autumn
(Rushes)	Use standard methods.	
Kennedia species	Seed	All year
	Softwood cuttings	Spring
	Seed should be treated in boiling water and soaked for 24 hours. Use standard methods.	
Kunzea species	Seed	Spring
	SHW cuttings	Autumn
	Seed is shed as soon as the fruit is ripe and will keep for at least a year. Use standard methods.	
Lachnostachys species	SHW cuttings	Autumn
(Lambstails)	Seed	Spring
	Because of the dense hairs do not place under mist, use a humidity tent. Smoke treatments have been successful for some species.	
Lagunaria pattersonii	Seed	Spring
(Norfolk Island hibiscus)	Take care when collecting seed as there are hairs around the seeds which can irritate skin. Seed germinates readily.	
Lambertia species	Seed	Spring
(Wild Honeysuckles)	SHW cuttings	Autumn
	Use standard methods. Seed can be extracted by heat treating fruits as for Banksia. Seed germinates without pretreatment.	
Lasiopetalum species	SHW cuttings	Autumn
(Velvet Bushes)	Use standard methods. Use as little mist as possible as cuttings are prone to rot caused by botrytis.	
Lechenaultia species	Softwood cuttings	Spring
	Seed	Spring

	Use standard methods. Smoke treatment is succcessful for a number of species. Embryo culture has been successful also.	
***Lepidosperma* species** (Rapier-sedges)	Seed	Spring
	Sow seed fresh. It may take many weeks to germinate. Smoke treatment would be worth trying.	
***Leptospermum* species** (Tea trees)	Seed	Spring to summer
	SHW cuttings	Autumn
	Use standard methods.	
***Leucopogon* species** (beard-heaths)	SHW cuttings	Autumn
	Seed	Spring
	Use standard methods. Smoke treatments would be worth trying.	
Libertia paniculata (Branching Grass-flag)	Division	Autumn
	Seed	Spring to Autumn
	Use standard methods.	
Licuala ramsayi (Fan Palm)	Seed	Any time
	Seed must be sown fresh and may take up to a year to germinate and is best done under greenhouse conditions.	
Livistona australis (Cabbage Palm)	Seed	Any time
	Seed must be sown fresh and may take up to a few months to germinate.	
***Lobelia* species**	Seed	Autumn
	Softwood cuttings	Spring
	Use standard methods.	
***Lomandra* species** (Mat Rushes)	Seed	Spring to Autumn
	Division	Autumn
	Fruits can beharvested into a paper bag which is shaken vigorously to dislodge seed. Sow seed fresh with no pretreatment. Use standard methods for division.	
***Lomatia* species**	Seed	Spring
	SHW cuttings	Summer to Autumn
	Sow seed fresh with no pretreatment. Use standard methods.	
Lophostemon confertus (Brush Box)	Seed	Spring
	Grafting or budding	Winter to spring
	Use standard methods. Seed retains viability for many years. These methods used for propagating variegated forms using normal forms of *L. confertus* as the rootstock.	
***Lycopodium* species**	Softwood cuttings	Spring to summer

(Tassel Ferns)	Stem tips are taken and laid horizontally on the propagation mix.	
Macadamia species	Seed	Spring
	Grafting Budding	Winter Spring
	Remove seed from shell and sow fresh. Cultivars of *M. tetraphylla* and *M. integrifolia* can be budded or grafted onto seedling rootstocks of *M. tetraphylla.*	
Macropidia fuliginosa	Seed	Spring
(Black Kangaroo Paw)	Micropropagation	All year
	Smoke treatment is succcessful for this species. Tissue culture is used for commercial production.	
Macrozamia species	Seed	All year
(Zamias)	Seed can take up to 2 years to germinate. Sow with half the seed protruding from the medium.	
Maireana species	Seed	Spring to summer
(Bluebushes)	Use standard methods. May take many weeks to germinate.	
Melaleuca.species	Seed	Spring
(Paperbarks, Honey-myrtles)	See *Callistemon*.	
Melastoma species	Seed	Spring
	Softwood cuttings	Spring
	Use standard methods.	
Melia azedarach	Seed	Spring
(White Cedar)	Use standard methods.	
Micromyrtus species	SHW cuttings	Autumn
	Use standard methods.	
Milletia species	Seed	Spring
(Native Wistaria)	Use boiling water treatment to break the hard seed coat.	
Mimulus species	Softwood cuttings	Spring
(Monkey-flowers)	Use standard methods.	
Muehlenbeckia species	Softwood cuttings	Spring
(Lignums)	Use standard methods.	
Myoporum species	SHW cuttings	Autumn
(Boobiallas)	Seed	Spring
	Use standard methods. Sow seed fresh.	
Nephrolepis species	Spores	All year
	Division	Spring
	See *Adiantum* for details. Use standard methods.	
Nothofagus species	Seed	Autumn

(Beeches)	Use standard methods. For species from very cold climates stratify seed at 2–5°C for 4 weeks before sowing.	
Nuytsia floribunda	Seed	Spring
(Christmas Tree)	Use standard methods.	
***Nymphaea* species**	Seed	Spring to Autumn
(Waterlilies)	Division	Autumn
	Micropropagation	All year
	Use standard methods for seeds and division. Microprogations is useful for outastanding clones.	
***Olearia* species**	SHW cuttings	Summer to Autumn
(Daisybushes)	Seed	Spring to Summer
	Use standard methods. Species from very cold climates should be stratified at 2–5°C for 4 weeks before sowing.	
Omalanthus nutans	Seed	Spring
(Bleeding Heart)	Softwood cuttings	Spring
	Sow seed fresh. Use standard methods. Use standard methods for cuttings.	
Orthrosanthus laxus	Division	Autumn
(Morning Iris)	Seed	Spring to Summer
	Use standard methods. Seed may take many weeks to germinate.	
***Oxylobium* species**	Seed	Spring
	Treat seed with boiling water before sowing.	
***Ozothamnus* species**	Seed	Spring
(Tree Everlastings)	Softwood cuttings	Spring
	Use standard methods. Species from very cold climates should be stratified at 2–5°C for 4 weeks before sowing. Use standard methods for cuttings.	
***Pandanus* species**	Seed	Spring to Autumn
(Screw Pines)	Sow seed fresh. It may take 6–12 months to germinate.	
***Pandorea* species**	Seed	Summer to Autumn
	Softwood cuttings	Spring to Summer
	Sow seed fresh. Use standard methods. Use standard methods for cuttings.	
***Parsonsia* species**	Seed	Spring
(Silkpods)	Softwood cuttings	Spring to Summer
	Sow seed fresh. Use standard methods. Use standard methods for cuttings.	

***Passiflora* species**	Seed	Summer to Autumn
(Passion Flowers)	Softwood cuttings	Spring to Summer
	Sow seed fresh. Use standard methods. Use standard methods for cuttings.	
***Patersonia* species**	Seed	Summer to Autumn
(Purple Flags)	Division	Autumn
	Sow seed fresh. Use standard methods. Use standard methods for division.	
***Pelargonium* species**	Seed	Spring to Autumn
	Softwood cuttings	Spring to Summer
	Use standard methods.	
Pennisetum alopecuroides	Seed	Spring to Autumn
(Swamp Foxtail)	Use standard methods.	
***Persoonia* species**	Softwood cuttings	Spring
(Geebungs)	Juvenile growth resulting from hard pruning has given best results for many species.	
***Petrophile* species**	Seed	Spring
(Conesticks)	SHW cuttings	Summer to Autumn
	Smoke treatment is successful for a number of species. Use standard methods. Rooting may take a number of months.	
***Phaius* species**	Seed	All year
(Swamp Orchids)	Division	Autumn
	Seed is sown in tissue culture. Use standard methods for division.	
***Phebalium* species**	SHW cuttings	Autumn
	Use standard methods.	
***Philotheca* species**	Softwood cuttings	Summer
	Use standard methods. Cuttings are best taken just as the wood starts to harden.	
***Pimelea* species**	Softwood cuttings	Spring
(Rice-flowers)	Use standard methods.	
***Pittosporum* species**	SHW cuttings	Autumn
	Seed	Summer to Autumn
	Use standard methods. Seed germinates very erratically.	
***Pityrodia* species**	Seed	Spring
(Native Foxgloves)	Softwood to SHW cuttings	Summer to Autumn
	Smoke treatment would be worth trying. Cuttings are hairy and rot easily so mist treatments should be kept to a minimum.	

***Platycerium* species**	Spore	All year
(Elkhorn Ferns)	Micropropagation	All year
	See *Adiantum* for method. Use standard methods.	
***Platysace* species**	SHW cuttings	Summer to Autumn
	Use standard methods.	
***Plectranthus* species**	Softwood cuttings	Spring to Summer
	Use standard methods.	
***Poa* species**	Seed	Spring to Summer
(Tussock-grasses)	Division	Spring
	Use standard methods for seed. Take large sections when dividing.	
***Podocarpus* species**	Seed	Spring
	SHW cuttings	Summer to Autumn
	Sow seed fresh. Use standard methods.	
***Pomaderris* species**	Softwood cuttings	Spring
	Use standard methods.	
Pratia pedunculata	Division	Spring to Summer
	Use standard methods.	
***Prostanthera* species**	Softwood cuttings	Spring to Summer
(Australian mint bushes)	Grafting	Early Spring
	Use standard methods. Top cleft graft is done using *Westringia fruticosa* as the rootstock.	
***Pterostylis* species**	Division	Early Spring
(Greenhood Orchids)	Use standard methods.	
***Ptilotus* species**	Seed	Spring to Summer
(Pussy's Tails)	Germination may be erratic and a lengthy process. Smoke treatments would be worth trying on difficult species.	
***Pultenaea* species**	Seed	Spring
	Treat seed with boiling water.	
***Ranunculus* species**	Seed	Spring to Summer
	Use standard methods.	
***Regelia* species**	Seed	Spring
	SHW cuttings	Autumn
	Use standard methods.	
***Restio* species**	Seed	Spring to Summer
	Smoke treatments have been successful with a number of species.	
Rhaphidophora	Softwood cuttings	Spring to Summer

australasica	Use standard methods.	
Rhododendron lochae	SHW cuttings	Autumn
	Use standard methods.	
Ricinocarpos pinifolius	SHW cuttings	Autumn
(Wedding Bush)	Cuttings are very difficult to strike. Young, juvenile growth has given best results.	
***Rubus* species**	Softwood	Spring
(Native Raspberries)	or SHW cuttings	Summer to Autumn
	Use standard methods.	
***Rulingia* species**	SHW cuttings	Summer to Autumn
	Use standard methods.	
Santalum acuminatum	Seed	Spring
(Quandong)	Germination is difficult. Some success has been achieved using 1-year-old seed. Seed is placed in moist peat and kept in the dark at 16–20°C until germination occurs.	
***Sarcochilus* species**	Micropropagation using seed	All year
	Seed is sown in sterile culture.	
***Scaevola* species**	Softwood cuttings	Spring to Autumn
(Fan Flowers)	Layering	
	Use standard methods. Use simple layering.	
Schefflera actinophylla	SHW cuttings	Summer to Autumn
(Umbrella Tree)	Use standard methods. It may be necessary to remove the soft growing tip to prevent wilting.	
***Scholtzia* species**	SHW cuttings	Summer to Autumn
	Use standard methods.	
***Scirpus* species**	Division	Summer to Autumn
	Use standard methods. Take large sections with many shoots.	
Scleranthus biflorus	Division	Spring
	Take large sections with many shoots. Use standard methods.	
Sloanea australis	Seed	Spring
(Maiden's Blush)	Sow seed fresh. Use standard methods.	
***Smilax* species**	Softwood cuttings	Spring to Summer
	Use standard methods.	
***Solanum* species**	Seed	Spring to Summer
	Softwood cuttings	Spring
	Sow seed fresh. Use standard methods for cuttings.	
Sollya heterophylla	Softwood cuttings	Spring to Summer
	Use standard methods.	

Spinifex hirsutus	Seed	Spring to Autumn
	Use standard methods.	
Sprengelia incarnata	SHW cuttings	Autumn
	Use standard methods. Cuttings are difficult to strike and will benefit from standard auxin treatment for SHW cuttings.	
Spyridium species	SHW cuttings	Autumn
	Use standard methods.	
Stackhousia species	Division	Autumn
	Use standard methods. Take large sections.	
Stenocarpus sinuatus (Queensland firewheel tree)	Seed	Spring
	Sow seed fresh. Use standard methods.	
Stipa species	Seed	Spring to Autumn
	Use standard methods.	
Stylidium species (Triggerplants)	Seed	Spring to Summer
	Division	Autumn
	Use standard methods.	
Stypandra species	Division	Autumn
	Use standard methods. Take large pieces.	
Styphelia species	SHW cuttings	Summer to Autum
	Use standard methods. Cuttings are difficult to strike.	
Swainsona species (now includes Sturt's desert pea)	Seed	Spring
	Softwood cuttings	Spring
	Seed should be treated with boiling water. Use standard methods for cuttings, except for species that are very hairy. These should be done without misting.	
Syncarpia glomulifera (Turpentine)	Seed	Spring
	Use standard methods.	
Syzygium species (Lillypillies)	Seed	Spring
	SHW cuttings	Autumn
	Seed should be sown fresh. Cultivars must be grown by cuttings. Use standard methods.	
Tasmannia species	SHW cuttings	Autumn
	Use standard methods.	
Tecomanthe hillii	Softwood cuttings	Spring to summer
	Use standard methods.	
Telopea species (Waratahs)	Seed	Spring
	SHW to Hardwood cuttings	Autumn to winter
	Use standard methods. Single node hardwood cuttings have	

been successfully used.

Templetonia retusa	Seed	Spring
	Treat seed with boiling water.	
***Tetratheca* species**	Softwood to SHW cuttings	Spring to Autumn
(Black-eyed Susans)	Use standard methods.	
***Thelymitra* species**	Seed	All year
(Sun Orchids)	Seed should be sown in sterile tissue culture conditions.	
***Thomasia* species**	Softwood cuttings	Spring
	Use standard methods.	
***Thryptomene* species**	Softwood to SHW cuttings	Spring to Autumn
	Use standard methods.	
***Thysanotus* species**	Seed	Spring to Autumn
(Fringe Lilies)	Smoke treatments would be worth trialling. Seeds have dormancy problems.	
Toona ciliata	Seed	Spring
(Australian red cedar)	Seed should be sown fresh. Use standard methods.	
Trachymene caerulea	Seed	Autumn to Spring
(Rottnest Island Daisy)	Use standard methods. Seed should be fresh.	
***Tristaniopsis* species**	Seed	Spring
	Use standard methods.	
Trochocarpa laurina	SHW cuttings	Autumn
	Use standard methods.	
***Verticordia* species**	Softwood to SHW cuttings	Autumn
(Featherflowers)	Seed	Spring
	Use standard methods. Smoke treatments have been successful with some species.	
Viminaria juncea	Seed	Spring to summer
(Native Broom)	Seed should be treated with boiling water.	
Viola betonicifolia	Seed	Autumn
V. hederacea	Division	Spring, summer, autumn
(Native Violets)	Use standard methods.	
***Vitex trifolia* 'Purpurea'**	SHW cuttings	Autumn
	Use standard methods.	
***Wahlenbergia* species**	Seed	Autumn
(Native Bluebells)	Division	Autumn
	Softwood cuttings	Spring
	Seed is best method for *W. stricta*. Cutting methods apply to perennial species such as *W. gloriosa*.	

***Westringia* species**	Softwood cuttings	Spring
	Use standard methods.	
Woollsia pungens	Softwood to SHW cuttings	Summer to Autumn
	Use standard methods. Roots are very fine and need to be handled carefully.	
***Xanthorrhoea* species** (Grass Trees)	Seed	Spring
	Use standard methods.	
***Xanthosia* species** (Southern Crosses)	Softwood	Spring
	Use standard methods.	
Xanthostemon chrysanthus *(Golden Penda)*	Seed	Spring
	Use standard methods. Sow seed as fresh as possible.	
***Xylomelum* species** (Woody Pears)	Seed	Spring to Summer
	Use standard methods. Seed can be extracted from fruit by applying heat treatment.	
***Zieria* species**	Softwood to SHW cuttings	Summer to Autumn
	Use standard methods.	

Table 2:
Propagation Methods for Exotic Species

Note: This is by no means an exhaustive list. It is intended to cover the most popular garden plants in Australia. More extensive listings are available in various overseas plant propagation books.

Plant name	Propagation method	Time of year
Abelia species	Softwood cuttings	Spring
	Use standard methods.	
Acalypha wilkesiana	Softwood cuttings	Spring to Summer
(Fijian Fire Bush)	Use standard methods.	
Acanthus mollis	Division	Autumn
(Oyster Plant)	Use standard methods.	
Acer species	Seed	Spring
(Maples)	Budding	
	Seed is harvested in autumn and stratified at 2–4°C for about 90 days. In spring sow by standard methods. Maple cultivars are generally T-budded onto understocks of the same species (e.g. *Acer palmatum* cultivars are budded onto seedling forms of that species).	
Achillea species	Softwood cuttings	Spring
(Yarrow)	Use standard methods.	
Agapanthus species	Division	Autumn
and cultivars	Seed	Spring
	Use standard methods.	
Agave species	Division	Autumn
(Century Plant)	Seed	Spring
	Use standard methods.	
Ageratum species	Seed	Autumn
	Use standard methods.	
Ajuga species and cultivars	Division	Spring
(Floss Flower)	Use standard methods.	
Allium species	Seed	Autumn
(Ornamental Onions)	Separation	Autumn
	Use standard methods.	
Alstroemeria species	Seed	Autumn
and cultivars	Division	Autumn

(Peruvian Lillies)	Soak seed for 48 hours before sowing for enhanced germination. Use standard methods.	
Alyssum species	Seed	Autumn
(Sweet Alice)	Division	All year
	Use standard methods.	
Amaryllis belladonna	Separation	Summer
(Belladonna Lily)	Seed	Spring
	Use standard methods.	
Anemone species	Seed	Autumn
	Division	Autumn
	Use standard methods.	
Antirrhinum species	Seed	Autumn to Spring
(Snapdragon)	Use standard methods.	
Apium graveolens	Seed	Autumn
(Celery)	Use standard methods.	
Aquilegia species	Seed	Autumn
(Granny's Bonnets	Division	Autumn
Columbines)	Do not cover seed. Use standard methods for division.	
Aster species	Division	Late Spring
(Perennial Aster)	Softwood cuttings	Spring
	Use standard methods.	
Azaleas	see *Rhododendron*	
Babiana species	Separation	Autumn
(Baboon Flower)	Use standard methods.	
Bamboos	Division	Late Winter
	Use standard methods.	
Begonia species	Seed	All year
and hybrids	Softwood cuttings	All year
	Leaf cuttings	All year
	Sow in greenhouse. Many species need light to germinate so do not cover seed but keep moist, preferably by misters. Use standard methods for cuttings.	
Bellis perennis	Seed	Autumn
	Division	Autumn
	Use standard methods.	
Betula pendula	Seed	Spring
(Silver Birch)	Seed is harvested in autumn and stratified at 2–4°C for about 90 days. In spring sow by standard methods.	

***Bougainvillea* species**	Hardwood cuttings	All year
	Use standard methods.	
***Bouvardia* species**	Softwood cuttings	Spring to Summer
	Use standard methods.	
Bromeliads	Division	Spring
	Use standard methods.	
Brunfelsia latifolia (Yesterday, Today and Tomorrow)	Softwood to SHW cuttings	Spring Autumn
	Use standard methods.	
***Buddleia* species** (Butterfly Bush)	Softwood cuttings	Spring
	Use standard methods.	
***Buxus* species** (Boxes)	SHW cuttings	Autumn
	Use slightly higher rates of rooting hormone than is normal for SHW cuttings, e.g. 5000–10 000 ppm IBA.	
***Caladium* species**	Division	Spring
	Use standard methods.	
***Calceolaria* species**	Seed	Autumn
	Use standard methods.	
Callistephus chinensis (China Aster)	Seed	Spring
	Use standard methods.	
***Camellia* species and cultivars**	SHW cuttings	Autumn
	Grafting	Late Winter
	Seed	Winter to Spring
	The use of rooting hormone is recommended with up to 10 000 ppm IBA. Cultivars of the very large flowered but not so hardy *C. reticulata* are sometimes grafted onto seedlings of the hardy *C. sasanqua* using the top cleft or wedge graft technique. Sow seed fresh. Use standard methods.	
***Campanula* species** (Bluebells)	Seed	Autumn
	Division	Autumn
	Use standard methods.	
***Canna* species** (Canna Lily)	Division	Spring
	Use standard methods.	
***Ceanothus* species**	Softwood cuttings	Spring
	Use standard methods.	
***Cedrus* species** (Cedars)	Seed	Spring
	Grafting	Late Winter
	Use standard methods. *Cedrus atlantica* forms are side veneer	

	grafted onto *C. deodara*.	
Celosia species	Seed	Spring
(Cockscombs)	Use standard methods.	
Centaurea species	Seed	Summer
(Cornflowers)	Use standard methods.	
Ceratostigma	Softwood cuttings	Spring
willmottianum	Use standard methods.	
Chrysanthemum	*see Dendranthema* species and hybrids	
Citrus species	Budding	Autumn
and cultivars	Most types of citrus are propagated by T-budding in autumn using a number of different rootstocks. Perhaps the hardiest of all rootstocks is the trifoliate orange (*Poncirus trifoliata*) which is compatible with most cultivars and is easily propagated from seed. One of the great problems with vegetative propagation is the transmission of viruses through budwood and for this reason it is important to obtain certified disease-free budwood for commercial propagation.	
Clivia species	Seed	Summer
	Division	Autumn
	Use standard methods.	
Coleonema species	Softwood cuttings	Spring
(Diosma)	Use standard methods.	
Coleus blumei	Seed	Spring
	Softwood cuttings	All year
	Use standard methods. Sow in greenhouse conditions.	
Cosmos bipinnatus	Seed	Spring to Summer
	Use standard methods.	
Cupressus species	Seed	Spring
(Cypress)	Seed is harvested in autumn and stratified at 2–4°C for about 4 weeks. In spring sow by standard methods.	
Dahlia species	Division	Winter
and hybrids	Root tubers are divided when the plants are lifted after flowering. Each tuber must have a swollen 'eye' (vegetative bud) at the top to be successful.	
Daphne species	SHW cuttings	Summer to Autumn
	Use standard methods.	
Delphinium species	Seed	Autumn
and hybrids	Softwood cuttings	Spring

	Division	Late Winter
	Seed should be covered with hessian or a similar material to ensure total darkness until it starts to germinate. Take emerging tips when new growth starts in spring. Use standard methods for cuttings and division.	
Dendranthema species and hybrids	Softwood cuttings	Spring to Summer
	Use standard methods.	
Dianthus species and cultivars	Softwood cuttings	Spring to Autumn
	Use standard methods.	
Dieffenbachia species (Dumb Cane)	Softwood cuttings	Spring to Summer
	Micropropagation	All year
	Use standard methods for cuttings. For micropropagation use apical or axillary buds and follow standard methods.	
Dietes species	Division	Autumn
	Use standard methods.	
Dracaena species (Happy Plant)	Hardwood cuttings	All year
	Use standard methods.	
Duranta erecta	SHW cuttings	Autumn
	Use standard methods.	
Echinacea species	Seed	Autumn
	Use standard methods.	
Erica species	SHW cuttings	Summer to Autumn
	Seed	Spring
	Use standard methods. Seed of many species responds to smoke treatment. Use standard methods.	
Erigeron species	Seed	Autumn
	Softwood cuttings	Spring to Summer
	Use standard methods.	
Euonymus japonica	SHW cuttings	Autumn
	Use standard methods.	
Euphorbia pulcherrima (Poinsettia)	Softwood cuttings	Spring to Summer
	Use standard methods.	
Fagus species (Beechs)	Seed	Spring
	Seed is harvested in autumn and stratified at $2-4°C$ for about 90 days. In spring sow by standard methods.	
Felicia amellioides	Softwood cuttings	Spring to Autumn
	Use standard methods.	
Ficus species	SHW cuttings	Summer to Autumn

(Figs)	Use standard methods.	
Fragaria species	Division	Autumn
(Strawberry)	Runners are taken from the parent plant and treated as cuttings.	
Fuchsia species	Softwood cuttings	Spring to Autumn
and cultivars	Use standard methods.	
Fraxinus species	Seed	Spring
(Ashes)	Seed is harvested in autumn and stratified at 2–4°C for about 90 days. In spring sow by standard methods.	
Freesia species	Separation	Autumn
	Use standard methods.	
Gaillardia species	Seed	Autumn
(Indian Blanket)	Softwood cuttings	Spring
	Use standard methods.	
Gardenia species	SHW cuttings	Autumn
and cultivars	Layering	Spring
	Seed is harvested in autumn and stratified at 2–4°C for about 90 days. In spring sow by standard methods. Low branches can also be readily propagated by simple or tip layering.	
Gazania species	Seed	Autumn
	Division	Autumn
	Use standard methods.	
Geranium	see *Pelargonium* species	
Gerbera jamesonii	Seed	Autumn
(Transvaal Daisy)	Division	Late Winter
	Use standard methods. Take large pieces.	
Ginkgo biloba	Seed	Spring
(Maidenhair Tree)	Seed is harvested in autumn and stratified at 2–4°C for about 90 days. In spring sow by standard methods.	
Gladiolus species	Separation	Autumn
and hybrids	Use standard methods.	
Gleditsia triacanthos	Seed	Spring
(Honey Locust)	Soak seed in boiling water before sowing.	
Gloxinia	(see *Sinningia*)	
Godetia species	Seed	Spring
	Use standard methods.	
Gordonia axillaris	SHW cuttings	Autumn
	Use standard methods.	

Gypsophila paniculata	Softwood cuttings	Spring
(Baby's Breath)	Use standard methods.	
Hebe **species**	SHW cuttings	Autumn
	Seed is harvested in autumn and stratified at 2–4°C for about 90 days. In spring sow by standard methods.	
Hedera **species**	Softwood cuttings	Spring to Summer
and cultivars (Ivy)	Use standard methods.	
Helianthus **species**	Seed	Spring
(Sunflowers)	Use standard methods. Direct sow into final position in garden if possible.	
Helleborus **species**	Seed	Spring
(Winter Roses)	Division	Spring
	Use standard methods.	
Hemerocallis **species**	Division	Late Winter
(Daylilies)	Use standard methods.	
Hibiscus **species**	SHW cuttings	Autumn
and cultivars	Use standard methods.	
Hippeastrum **species**	Separation	Spring
and hybrids	Use standard methods.	
Hosta **species**	Division	Spring
	Use standard methods.	
Hoya **species**	Softwood cuttings	Spring to Summer
and cultivars	Use standard methods.	
Hydrangea **species**	Softwood cuttings	Spring
and cultivars	Hardwood cuttings	Winter
	Soft tip cuttings can be taken from mid to late spring and can be well established before the plants lose their leaves for winter. In a home garden situation it is probably easiest to take hardwood cuttings in winter and these can even be planted directly into soil in the garden although establishing them in pots first is a wise precaution.	
Hypericum **species**	Softwood cuttings	Spring to Summer
(St John's Wort)	Use standard methods.	
Impatiens **species**	Seed	All year
(Busy Lizzie)	Softwood cuttings	Spring to Summer
	Use standard methods.	
Iris **species**	Division	Autumn
and hybrids	Separation	Autumn

Division for bearded and Louisiana Iris types. Use standard methods. Separation for Dutch iris types. Use standard methods.

***Ixia* species** (Corn Lilies)	Separation	Autumn
	Use standard methods.	
Jacaranda mimosifolia	Seed	Spring
	Budding	Spring to Autumn
	Use standard methods. A rare white flowered form of this species is readily propagated by T-budding.	
***Jasminum* species and cultivars** (Jasmines)	Softwood cuttings	Spring to Summer
	Use standard methods.	
***Juniperus* species**	SHW cuttings	Summer to Autumn
	Use standard methods.	
***Justicia* species**	Softwood cuttings	Spring to Summer
	Use standard methods.	
***Kalanchoe* species**	Softwood cuttings	All Year
	Leaf cuttings	All Year
	Use standard methods. Leaf and petiole cuttings are successful for some species.	
***Kniphofia* species** (Red Hot Pokers)	Division	Autumn to Spring
	Seed	Autumn
	Use standard methods.	
***Lachenalia* species** (Soldier Boys)	Separation	Autumn
	Use standard methods.	
Lagerstroemia indica (Crepe Myrtle)	Softwood cuttings	Winter
	Hardwood cuttings	Spring to Summer
	Use standard methods. Misting facilities are essential for softwood cuttings.	
***Lamium* species**	Softwood cuttings	Spring to Summer
	Division	Spring
	Use standard methods.	
Lathyrus odoratus (Sweet Pea)	Seed	Autumn
	Use standard methods.	
***Lavandula* species** (Lavenders)	Softwood cuttings	Spring to Summer
	Use standard methods. With very hairy species misting should be kept to an absolute minimum.	
***Leucadendron* species**	SHW cuttings	Autumn
	Use standard methods.	

***Liatris* species**	Seed	Spring
(Gay Feathers)	Division	Autumn
	Use standard methods.	
***Lilium* species**	Separation	Autumn
(Lillies)	Use standard methods.	
***Limonium* species**	Seed	Spring
(Statice)	Division	Spring
	Use standard methods.	
Liquidambar styraciflua	Seed	Spring
(Liquidamber)	Seed is harvested in autumn and stratified at 2–4°C for about 90 days. In spring sow by standard methods.	
***Lisianthus* species**	Seed	Spring
(Prairie Gentian)	Use standard methods.	
***Lobelia* species**	Seed	Autumn
	Softwood cuttings	Spring
	Use standard methods. Best method for annual species.	
***Lonicera* species**	Softwood cuttings	Spring to Summer
(Honeysuckles)	Use standard methods.	
***Lupinus* species**	Seed	Spring
(Lupins)	Use standard methods. Species with hard seed coats may need scarification treatment such as soaking in boiling water.	
Lycoris aurea	Separation	Spring
(Golden Spider Lily)	Use standard methods.	
***Magnolia* species and hybrids**	Seed	Autumn
	Softwood cuttings	Spring to Summer
	Layering	Spring
	Sow seed immediately. Species from cold climates should be stratified at 4°C for 2–3 months. Use standard methods. Suitable for species such as *M. soulangeana* and *M. stellata*. Simple layering works well for most species and cultivars.	
***Malus* species and cultivars**	Budding	Spring or Autumn
	Seed	Autumn
(Apples and Crabapples)	T-budding is used for apples and clonal types of Crabapple with a wide variety of rootstocks used including clonal forms to achieve effects such as dwarfing of the mature tree. Crabapple species are also propagated from seed which germinates readily without any treatment.	
***Mandevilla* species**	Softwood cuttings	Spring

217

	Use standard methods.	
Matthiola incana	Seed	Autumn
(Stock)	Use standard methods.	
Melia azedarach	Seed	Autumn
(White Cedar)	Use standard methods.	
Metasequoia	Seed	Autumn
glyptostroboides	Use standard methods. Seed germinates freely.	
(Dawn Redwood)		
Metrosideros species	Seed	Spring
and cultivars	SHW cuttings	Summer to Autumn
	Use standard methods. Cultivars must be propagated by cuttings.	
Molucella laevis	Seed	Autumn
(Bells of Ireland)	Use standard methods.	
Murraya paniculata	SHW cuttings	Autumn
(Orange Jessamine)	Use standard methods.	
Nandina domestica	SHW cuttings	Autumn
and cultivars	Use standard methods.	
Narcissus species	Separation	Autumn
and cultivars	Use standard methods.	
(Daffodils and Jonquils)		
Nelumbo species	Division	Autumn
(Sacred Lotus)	Use standard methods.	
Nephrolepis species	Division	Spring to Summer
and cultivars (Boston Ferns)	Use standard methods.	
Nerine species	Separation	Spring
and cultivars	Use standard methods.	
Nerium oleander	SHW cuttings	Summer
(Oleander)	Use standard methods.	
Nigella damascena	Seed	Autumn
(Love in a Mist)	Use standard methods.	
Olea species	SHW cuttings	Autumn
(Olives)	Use standard methods.	
Ophiopogon japonicus	Division	All year
(Mondo Grass)	Use standard methods.	
Origanum species	Softwood cuttings	Spring to Autumn
(Marjoram)	Use standard methods.	
Ornithogalum species	Separation	Autumn

(Chincherinchees)	Use standard methods.	
Osmanthus fragrans	SHW cuttings	Summer
	Use standard methods.	
***Osteospermum* species**	Softwood cuttings	Spring to Summer
	Use standard methods.	
***Paeonia* species**	Division	Autumn
(Paeonies)	Use standard methods.	
***Papaver* species**	Seed	Summer
(Poppies)	Use standard methods.	
***Parthenocissus* species**	Hardwood cuttings	Winter
(Virginia Creeper and	Use standard methods.	
Boston Ivy)		
***Passiflora* species**	Seed	Spring
(Passionfruit)	Grafting	Early Spring
	Use standard methods. Use top cleft graft onto Banana Passionfruit rootstock.	
***Pelargonium* species**	Softwood cuttings	Spring to Summer
(Geraniums)	Use standard methods.	
***Peperomia* species**	Softwood or Leaf cuttings	All year
	Use standard methods.	
***Penstemon* species**	Softwood cuttings	Spring
and cultivars	Seed	Autumn
	Use standard methods.	
***Petunia* species**	Seed	Autumn
and cultivars	Use standard methods.	
***Philadelphus* species**	Hardwood cuttings	Early Spring
(Mock Orange)	Softwood cuttings	Summer
	Use standard methods.	
***Philodendron* species**	Softwood cuttings	All year
	Use standard methods.	
***Photinia* species**	SHW cuttings	Autumn
	Use standard methods.	
Physostegia virginiana	Softwood cuttings	Spring to Summer
(Obedient plant)	Division	Spring
	Use standard methods.	
***Picea* species**	Seed	Spring
(Spruces)	Grafting	Autumn
	Seed is harvested in autumn and stratified at 2–4°C for about	

90 days. In spring sow by standard methods. Blue Spruce cultivars are side veneer grafted onto *Picea abies* rootstock.

Pieris japonica	Seed	Spring
	Softwood cuttings	Spring
	Use standard methods.	
***Pilea* species**	Softwood cuttings	All year
	Use standard methods.	
***Pinus* species** (Pine trees)	Seed	Spring
	Most species germinate readily when seed is sown fresh. Species from cold climates may need to be stratified at 2–4°C for 1–4 months.	
***Platanus* species** (Plane Trees)	Seed	Spring
	Seed is harvested in autumn and stratified at 2–4°C for about 90 days. In spring sow by standard methods.	
***Plectranthus* species**	Softwood cuttings	Spring to Summer
	Use standard methods.	
Plumbago auriculata	Softwood cuttings	Spring to Summer
	Use standard methods.	
***Plumeria* species and cultivars**	Hardwood cuttings	Late Winter
	Use standard methods. Very thick woody sections can be used successfully.	
Polianthes tuberosa (Tuberose)	Separation	Spring
	Use standard methods.	
***Populus* species** (Poplars)	Hardwood cuttings	Late Winter
	Use standard methods.	
***Portulaca* species**	Seed	Spring
	Use standard methods.	
***Primula* species**	Seed	Autumn
	Use standard methods.	
***Protea* species**	Seed	Spring
	SHW cuttings	Autumn
	Sow seed fresh. Smoke treatment has been effective for species such as *P. compacta* and would be worth trying with other species. Use standard methods.	
***Prunus* species** (Blossom Trees)	Budding	Autumn
	Ornamental *Prunus* cultivars can be T-budded onto seedling rootstocks such as *P. serrulata* or *P. avium*.	
Prunus glandulosa	Hardwood cuttings	Late Winter

	Use standard methods.	
Prunus laurocerasus	SHW cuttings	Autumn
(Laurel)	Use standard methods.	
Punica granatum	Hardwood cuttings	Late Winter
(Pomegranate)	Use standard methods.	
***Pyracantha* species**	SHW cuttings	Summer
(Firethorn)	Use standard methods.	
Pyrostegia venusta	Softwood cuttings	Spring to Summer
	Use standard methods.	
***Quercus* species**	Seed	Spring
(Oaks)	A number of species germinate readily when seed is sown fresh. Species from cold climates may need to be stratified at 0–2°C for about 1–3months.	
***Ranunculus* species**	Seed	Autumn
and cultivars	Division	Autumn
	Use standard methods.	
***Rhododendron* species**	SHW cuttings	Summer to Autumn
and hybrids	Layering	Spring
(including Azaleas)	Use standard methods. Rhododendrons and azaleas are readily propagated by simple layering of branches growing close to the ground.	
***Rondeletia* species**	Softwood or	Spring
	SHW cuttings	Summer to Autumn
	Use standard methods.	
***Rosa* species**	Budding	Spring
and cultivars	Softwood cuttings	Spring to early summer
(Roses)	T-budding is most commonly used for rose cultivars with *R. multiflora* or *R. canina* being the most commonly used rootstocks. Use standard methods.	
Rosmarinus officinalis	SHW cuttings	Autumn
(Rosemary)	Use standard methods.	
***Rudbeckia* species**	Seed	Autumn
	Softwood cuttings	Spring to Summer
	Use standard methods.	
Saintpaulia ionantha	Leaf and Petiole cuttings.	All year
(African Violet)	Use standard methods. In the home garden a fascinating method is to fill a glass with water and cover it with aluminium foil held on by a rubber band. The petiole is then pushed	

through the foil which then holds it in place. Place the glass in an area that gets indirect light and is sheltered and wait for roots to form before potting it on.

Salix species (Willows)	Hardwood cuttings	Late Winter
	Use standard methods. Cuttings will root easily, even in water. Anecdotal evidence suggests that the water can be taken after the plants root and can be used as a root promoting treatment for dipping the ends of cuttings of other species.	
Salvia species	Seed	Autumn
	Softwood cuttings	Spring to Summer
	Use standard methods.	
Sansevieria species (Mother-in-law's Tongue)	Leaf cuttings	All year
	Cut leaf into numerous small segments and make sure to plant them with the correct orientation.	
Sapium sebiferum (Chinese Tallow Tree)	Seed	Spring
	Use standard methods.	
Scabiosa species	Softwood cuttings	Spring to Summer
	Use standard methods. Take non-flowering shoots.	
Schinus areira (Pepper Tree)	Seed	Spring
	Use standard methods.	
Scilla species	Separation	Autumn
	Use standard methods.	
Sedum species	Leaf cuttings	All year
	Softwood cuttings	All year
	Leaf cuttings are successful for a number of species such as *S. morganianum*. Use standard methods.	
Sinningia species (Gloxinia)	Seed	Spring
	Leaf cuttings	Spring
	Use standard methods but leave seed uncovered as they require light to germinate.	
Solandra guttata (Cup of Gold Vine)	SHW cuttings	Summer to Autumn
	Use standard methods.	
Solidago species (Goldenrod)	Softwood cuttings	Spring to Summer
	Use standard methods.	
Spiraea species (May bushes)	SHW cuttings	Summer
	Use standard methods.	
Stephanotis floribunda	Softwood cuttings	Spring to Summer
	Seed	Autumn

	Use standard methods. Sow fresh. Use standard methods.	
Strelitzia reginae	Seed	Spring
(Bird of Paradise)	Division	Autumn
	Soak seed for 72 hours before sowing. Use standard methods.	
Streptocarpus species	Leaf cuttings	All year
(Cape Violet)	Use standard methods.	
Tecomaria capensis	Softwood cuttings	Spring to Summer
	Use standard methods.	
Thuja species	SHW cuttings	Late Winter
	Use standard methods.	
Thymus species	Softwood cuttings	Spring to Summer
(Thyme)	Division	Spring to Autumn
	Use standard methods.	
Tibouchina species	Softwood cuttings	Spring
and cultivars (Lasiandra)	Use standard methods.	
Tolmeia menziesii	Leaf cuttings	Spring to Autumn
(Piggyback Plant)	Take leaves that already have well-developed plantlets on them and insert the petiole from the parent leaf to anchor the plant in the medium.	
Torenia species	Seed	Autumn
	Use standard methods.	
Trachelospermum jasminoides (Star Jasmine)	Softwood cuttings	Spring
	Use standard methods.	
Tropaeolum majus	Seed	Autumn
(Nasturtium)	Use standard methods.	
Tulipa species and cultivars (Tulips)	Separation	Summer to Autumn
	Use standard methods. In warm climates lifted bulbs need to be refrigerated for 2 months at 2–4°C to obtain best flowering.	
Ulmus species	Seed	Spring
(Elms)	Seed is harvested in autumn and stratified at 2–4°C for about 90 days. In spring sow by standard methods.	
Vallota species	Separation	Autumn
(Scarborough Lily)	Use standard methods.	
Verbena species	Softwood cuttings	Spring to Summer
	Use standard methods.	
Viburnum species	SHW to Hardwood cuttings	Autumn to Winter
	Use standard methods.	

***Vinca* species**	Softwood cuttings	Spring to Summer
(Periwinkles)	Use standard methods.	
***Viola* species**	Seed	Autumn
and hybrids	Division	Spring to Summer
	Use standard methods. Use division for perennial species such as *V. hederacea* and *V. odorata*.	
***Vitis* species**	Hardwood cuttings	Late Winter
(Grapes)	Use leafless material. Cuttings can be planted outdoors and rooted in milder climates.	
***Watsonia* species**	Separation	Autumn
	Use standard methods.	
***Weigela* species**	Hardwood cuttings	Late Winter
(Weigelias)	Use leafless material but otherwise standard methods for hardwood cuttings.	
***Wisteria* species**	Softwood cuttings	Early Summer
	Layering	Spring
	Use standard methods for cuttings. Simple layering is extremely easy form low growing canes.	
***Yucca* species**	Seed	Spring
	Division	Autumn
	Use standard methods.	
***Zantedischia* species**	Division	Spring
(Calla Lilies)	Use standard methods.	
***Zephyranthes* species**	Separation	Spring
(Rain Lilies)	Use standard methods.	
***Zinnia* species**	Seed	Autumn
	Use standard methods.	

Plant Hormones, Plant Growth Regulators and Propagation

Biological control suppliers

Bugs for Bugs,
28 Orton St, Mundubbera, QLD 4626.
Phone (07) 4165 4663 Fax (07) 4165 4626.

Suppliers of beneficials to control mealybugs, caterpillars, aphids, thrips, whitefly, citrus mealybug, and various scale insects.

Biological Services,
PO Box 501, Loxton, South Australia 5333.
Phone (08) 8584 6977 Fax (08) 8584 5057.

Suppliers of beneficials to control whitefly, spider mites and scale insects.

Greennem,
PO Box 240, Monbulk, Victoria 3793.
Phone/Fax (03) 9756 6997

Suppliers of beneficial nematodes for control of fungus gnat larvae, army worm, curl grub and mole crickets.

Hawkesbury IPM Service,
PO Box 436, Richmond NSW 2753.
Phone/fax (02) 4570 1331.

Suppliers of predatory mites for spider mite pests.

The Seed Savers' Network is a non profit organisation whose aim is to pre-serve genetic diversity in food crops. It is run by Michel and Jude Fanton. The address is:

The Seed Savers' Network,
P.O. Box 975,
Byron Bay, NSW 2481
Australia.
Phone/fax (02) 6685 6624

Further Reading

Blombery, A.M., and Maloney, B., 1994. *Propagating Australian plants,* Kangaroo Press, Kenthurst, N.S.W.

Bowes, B.G., 1999. *A colour atlas of plant propagation and conservation,* Manson, London.

Bryant, G., 1995. *Growing plants for free,* Simon & Schuster, East Roseville, N.S.W.

Damiano, C., and Monticelli, S., 1998. *In vitro* fruit trees rooting by *Agrobacterium rhizogenes* wild type infection. Plant Biotechnology 3:1-8.

Debergh, P.C., and Zimmerman, R.H., (eds) 1991. *Micropropagation: technology and application,* Kluwer Academic, Dordrecht, Boston.

De Fossard, R.A., 1976. *Tissue Culture for Plant Propagators,* University of New England Printery, Armidale, N.S.W.

De Fossard, R.A., 1993. *Plant tissue culture propagation,* Xarma Pty. Ltd., Eagle Heights, Qld.

Eldridge, K., Davidson, J., Harwood, C. and van Wyk, G., 1994. *Eucalypt Domestication and Breeding*, Oxford Science Publications.

Garner, R.J., 1957. *The Grafter's Handbook*, Faber & Faber, London.

Garzoli, Keith, 1988. *Greenhouses: Handbook for Nurserymen, Horticulturalists and Gardeners*, AGPS Press, Canberra.

George, E.F., and Sherrington, P.D., *Plant propagation by tissue culture: handbook and directory of commercial laboratories,* Exegetics, Basingstoke George, E.F., *Plant propagation by tissue culture,* Exegetics, Edington, England.

Gorer, R., 1978. *Growing plants from seed,* Faber, London, Boston.

Hamrick, D., (ed) 1996. *GrowerTalks on plugs II,* 2nd ed. Ball Publishing, Batavia, Ill., USA:

Hartmann, H.T., Kester, D.E. and Davies F.T., 1990. *Plant Propagation: Principles and Practices*, Prentice-Hall, Englewood Cliffs, N.J., 5th edition.

Knudson, L., 1922. 'Nonsymbiotic Germination of Orchid Seeds', Bot. Gaz., 73, pp.1-15

Langkamp, Peter, (ed.) 1987. *Germination of Australian Native Plant Seed,* Inkata Press, Melbourne and Sydney.

Lindsay, P., 1981. *The Australian gardener's guide to propagation of trees & shrubs,* Reed, Frenchs Forest, N.S.W.

Macdonald, A.B., 1986. *Practical woody plant propagation for nursery growers,* Batsford, London.

Maynard, B., and Bassuk, N., 1988. 'Etiolation and Banding Effects on Adventitious Root Formation' in T.Davis, B. Haissig and N. Sankhla (eds), *Adventitious Root Formation in Cuttings,* Dioscorides Press, Portland, Oregon, pp. 47-60.

Murashige, T., and Skoog,F., 1962. 'A revised medium for rapid growth and bioassays with tobacco tissue cultures. Physiologia Plantarum 15:473-497.

Owen-Turner, J.C. and Shaw, R.G., 1984. *Citrus propagation in containers,* Queensland Dept. of Primary Industries, Brisbane.

Plumridge, J., 1976. *How to propagate plants,* Lothian, Melbourne.

Richards, D. and Beardsell, D., 1987. 'Seed Dormancy' in P.Langkamp (ed.), *Germination of Australian Native Plant Seed,* Inkata Press, Melbourne and Sydney, p.1-13.

Strobel, G., and Nachmias, A., 1988. '*Agrobacterium rhizogenes*: A Root Inducing Bacterium' in T.Davis, B. Haissig and N. Sankhla (eds), *Adventitious Root Formation in Cuttings,* Dioscorides Press, Portland, Oregon, pp. 284-88.

Taji, A. and Williams, R., (eds) 1996. *Tissue culture of Australian plants,* University of New England, Armidale, N.S.W.

Toogood, A.R., 1981. *Propagation,* Stein and Day, New York.

Watts, L., 1980. *Flower and vegetable plant breeding,* Grower Books, London.

Wright, R.C.M. and Titchmarsh A. 1981. The complete book of plant propagation: a practical guide to the various methods of propagating trees, shrubs, herbaceous plants, fruits and vegetables, Ward Lock, London.

Periodicals about Plant Propagation

The International Plant Propagators' Society is a world-wide network of people who share a passion for plant propagation. In addition to a regular newsletter, the society has annual regional meetings. The papers presented at these meetings are published in the Combined proceedings of the society. These proceedings stretch back to 1950 and they can be found in specialist agricultural and horticultural libraries. Details of the society can be found on the internet by searching for the society by name.

Index